S0-CFM-474

MAKE EYES
WITH MADELEINE MONO

Photographs by Torkil Gudnason
Illustrations by David Croland

Make Eyes with Madeleine Mono

Every Woman's Step-by-Step Guide to
Beautiful Eyes and Perfect Eye Makeup
for Day and Night

by Madeleine Mono

A & W VISUAL LIBRARY
NEW YORK

Picture Credits for Color Insert

Photographs by Torkil Gudnason. Models courtesy of the Elite Model Corporation/John Casablancas and the Wallace Agency. Makeup by Jim Kennedy. Hair by Janine Costa. "Colorscope" by Vicenta Aviles.

Night Eyes—model: Adelyne (Elite). *5-Minute Mistake-Proof Daytime Eye Makeup*—model: Patricia Skadeland (Elite). *The Gilded Eye*—model: Adelyne (Elite). *The Butterfly Eye*—model: Susan Thiele (Elite). *The Radiant Rainbow Eye*—model: Kelly Brennan (Elite); makeup: Gerard Merola. *The Eastern Eye*—model: Ariane (Elite); makeup: Gerard Merola. *The Sultry Eye*—model: Karin Adreasen. *The Over-30 Eye*—model: Jill Whitaker (Wallace). *The Over-40 Eye*—model: Keith Eager (Wallace). *The Over-60 Eye*—model: Mrs. Lily Mono; makeup: Pamela Goddard; hair: ELIO—The Cadogan Club; photography: Mario Testino.

Recipes and instructions appearing on pages 85, 117, 120 and 122 are quoted by permission from Clare Maxwell-Hudson's book *A Woman's Book of Nature's Beauty Secrets*, ©1976, Published by Autumn Press.

Copyright © 1981 by Madeleine Mono

All rights reserved. No part of this work may be reproduced or transmitted in any form or by any means, electronic or mechanical, including photocopying, recording, or any information storage and retrieval system, without permission in writing from the publisher.

An A & W Visual Library book
Published in 1982 by
A & W Publishers, Inc.
95 Madison Avenue
New York, NY 10016

By Arrangement with Harper & Row, Publishers, Inc.
Manufactured in the United States of America

Designed by J. Montebello
Cover design by Gloria Adelson/Lulu Graphics
Photograph of Madeleine Mono by Torkil Gudnason
Makeup by Gerard Merola

1 2 3 4 5 6 7 8 9 10

Library of Congress Catalog Card Number: 81-70451
ISBN 0-89104-294-6

Recipes and instructions appearing on pages 85, 117, 120 and 122 are quoted by permission from Clare Maxwell-Hudson's book A Woman's Book of Nature's Beauty Secrets, © 1976, published by Autumn Press.

To my darling husband, Arthur, who helped make my dream a reality

And to Iris Parnes, my only true friend,
who had beautiful eyes and a soul to match

Contents

Acknowledgments xi

Preface xiii

1/ My Philosophy on Eye Makeup and Beauty 3

2/ Eye Equipment 6

3/ Eyebrows and Eyelashes 21

4/ Eye Types 31

5/ The 5-Minute Mistake-Proof Daytime Eye Makeup 44

6/ Color 56

7/ Night Eyes 71

8/ Special Effect Theatrics / Special Occasion Eyes 81

9/ Eyeglasses and Contact Lenses 88

10/ Eye and Beauty Pharmacopoeia 104

11/ Eye Watch 121

Eyescope 137

Index 140

An insert of color photographs follows page 80.

Acknowledgments

THERE ARE SO MANY wonderful and creative people I would like to thank. Special people with vision, who took the time to listen to me and offered invaluable advice and encouragement. I give my heartwarming thanks to: Jacqueline Warsaw, a very real, warm, and lovely human being, whose writing knitted it all together for me; my editor, Nancy Crawford, who guided me in the right direction; Joseph Montebello, my art director, whose artistic input was invaluable; Torkil Gudnason, my photographer, whose loving attention to every detail produced pictures that speak for themselves; David Croland, my artist, who interpreted my thoughts with a sweep of his pencil; Jim Kennedy, my international training director, whose help in coordinating this book project was admirable; Janine Costa, my hair stylist and friend, whose enthusiasm and loyalty show in every hairdo she created for the book; and Gerard Merola, my creative makeup artist, whose talent is certainly one of a kind.

My book would not be complete unless I thanked my family, in the United States and England, who are a vital part of my business — all of us united by our common bonds of love for each other and the cosmetic industry: my husband, Arthur, Executive Vice-President; my mother, Lily Mono, my U.K. Press Representative; my father, Arthur, Chairman of the Board (U.K.), who stands behind us all and is our inspiration; my brother, Stephen, Managing Director (U.K.), who launched my cosmetics at the American Embassy in London in 1979, along with the help of his wife Patricia; Gail, my eldest daughter and look-alike, whose ideas are ahead of the times; my daughter Louise, Regional Manager (U.K.), who rallies to every call; my daughter Lesley, Co-director of International Training, who at age fourteen (eight years ago) had the insight, long before I did, that I was born for this business; my sons, Craig, Vice-President, and Grant, Purchasing Director, who help me run the company; and my daughter-in-law, Jane, whose creative efforts help grace my promotions.

To those in the retail business in the United States who gave me my chance, my sincere appreciation. Thanks to Karol Kempster of Henri Bendel, who gave me my first order and said, "You'll never forget me or this day!" I never have. Thanks also to the people at Bloomingdale's, who I hope are as fond of me as I am of them: Mike Blumenfeld, who gave me my first cosmetic counter—he believed in me and I hope he never regrets it—and Marvin Traub, Lester Grebitz, Rita McDonald, Pat Ennis, Arlene Friedman, Blanche Friedman, Alice Garment, Clelia Krishmar, and Candi Neiman. Thanks to Rosanne Cooper, Rosemary Bravo, and Grace Carrachino of Macy's, who made Herald Square in New York seem as familiar to me as Berkley Square in London. To Marilyn Bagbee, who gave me my first order at Macy's, New York, and is now with Jordan Marsh in Florida. Thanks to Carol Thomas and Gene Lewis of Lord & Taylor, New York, and Rose Waldman of Lord & Taylor, Boston.

My sincere thanks to those retailers in London who helped make me a star in my own home town: Mary Brogan of Selfridge's, Beryl Lake of Harvey Nichols, Pat Newell of Harrod's, and Norman Claire of Dickens & Jones.

My warm appreciation and thanks to my staff, without whom I couldn't have done it: Debbie Crawford, my dearest personal secretary, who holds me together as no one else ever could; Toni Napoli, Ron Wilks, Anthony Black, Esther Fiametta, Ronnay Jay, Andrea DiRienzio, Laura Williams, Bruce Hawkins, Maria Macheda, and Elizabeth Des Rochers; Eric Burgess, National Sales Director (U.K.); Jim Knowlton, Vice-President Sales (U.S.A.); all the line personnel, sales help, office staff, and packing department people who are essential to the success of the company.

My very special thanks to Shirley Lord of *Vogue,* who first introduced "Indian Eyes" to the women of America. Thanks also to: John Handler of the Great Neck *Newsmagazine,* who gave me my first opportunity to be a beauty editor; Dave and Toni Mitchell, who first brought me to the attention of Harper & Row; and Harry Doyle and Gerard Semhon, my encouraging friends in the cosmetic industry; Ira H. Kaufman, M.D., F.A.C.S., Associate Professor of Opthalmology, Cornell Medical College; Theresa Castro; Annette Steinberg of London Optical, Long Island, N.Y.; and Marjorie Kern.

Finally, to all those who said I could, I thank you. And to those who said I couldn't, I did!

Preface

ON OCTOBER 23, 1974, I walked into Henri Bendel, one of New York City's chic, high-fashion department stores, for an appointment with their cosmetic buyer. Little did I know that this meeting, which for a retailer is fairly routine and just one of dozens during an average week, would be a turning point in my life as well as in the lives of my entire family. I was thirty-nine years old at the time, and my life prior to that day had been spent in preparation to become the Madeleine Mono I was that day and to found the cosmetic empire I had long dreamed of building.

My childhood in London from the ages of twelve through eighteen was not very conventional. I attended Aida Foster's theatrical school and life was full of the magic of bright lights, applause, costumes, and makeup. I made my debut on the London stage the first year I was enrolled in theatrical school and quickly developed a reputation backstage as one of the youngest actresses around to have one of the best makeup collections anywhere. My mother bought me my first theatrical makeup and a small, black-tin professional box to keep it in. I wrote my name proudly inside the lid. I still have that box, and when I open it and smell the greasepaint it fills my mind with many marvelous memories of that time in my life. I adored the brushes, the colors, the paints and tints and highlighters. The glosses and glitter and glamour . . . all the seeds that would later germinate as the inspiration for my own cosmetics today. I loved the dramatic flair and fantasy of stage makeup even then — not because they transformed me from being me but because they *were* part of me. And still are.

Anyway, my theatrical career budded quickly and I was fortunate to get many good parts in plays and films as well as a fair number of fashion modeling assignments in between shows. But each of life's chapters — no matter how wonderful — comes to an end, and at the age of eighteen I abandoned my role as a young British actress to take on another — that of wife. Certainly a child bride by today's standards, I had four beautiful children in the first five years of marriage.

My days were happy, filled with raising and nurturing a wonderful family. I was even able to return to a modified acting career, doing TV commercials and other theatrical stints. Gradually, however, my love for the theater was eclipsed by yet another love — antiques. The third chapter of my life started when I opened an antique shop in the St. James district of London. I guess my entrepreneurial sense was keen even then, but I never thought of myself as a business woman in the traditional way. As far as I was concerned, working with antiques was something I loved, and that took it out of the category of work.

Shortly after the antique venture took off, what I had thought was a lifetime marriage contract ended after eighteen years, and with its end came the close of my life and work in England. I left everything behind when I divorced and not until I met my present husband, Arthur Levene, did I ever dream of what the fourth chapter of my life would be. It began shortly after my marriage to Arthur when I came to America to live.

I began thinking about what sort of job I could do. I had always been interested in my appearance and women often approached me asking, "How do you get that effect with your eyes?" or "Where did you buy your eye makeup?" My secret was the clever application of *kajal,* a vegetable substance used as a cosmetic by women in India, which I used to rim the inside of my eyes for a striking, sultry effect. One day a local beauty salon asked me if I would be willing to give makeup consultations to its clients. I said I would — but only if the women would first take off their false eyelashes. I firmly believed that false eyelashes belonged only on the stage — and that was a matter I did know something about. The women protested, naturally, but I insisted that I couldn't give them the "Mono look" unless they got rid of them. Well, we came to an agreement, and by the end of the first week I was booked so solid with clients and was having so much more fun than I'd ever had in my life, I knew I had to make a more serious commitment to beauty and cosmetics than just this. As it happened, the women couldn't get enough of my little magic bullets of Indian kajal. My husband innocently suggested that I start a company and market it along with some of my other cosmetic ideas. (Later, Arthur told me he thought it would be a nice hobby for me, something to keep me occupied. But, with the determination I apply to most ventures, and adventures, I decided to give it a go.)

I began building my cosmetic company on a shoestring capital investment of $7500 which Arthur invested in me. I started packaging and selling (by myself) that small kajal bullet. My first order, signed on October 23, 1974, came from Karol Kempster, Henri Bendel's cosmetic buyer. Shortly afterward, Bloomingdale's in New York began stocking the product and it sold out immediately. Madeleine Mono Ltd. was launched.

In retrospect, I really believe my success had a lot to do with some advice given to me by Robert Jacobsen of B. H. Krueger when I visited his offices. He told me that if I was to succeed I must not be a "Me too" or an "As well," but rather an innovator and trendsetter; that the best way for me to start my company would be to introduce one truly unique product and then try to build on it. Everything else would follow if that first step was successful, he predicted. I remember how breathless I was when I relayed Bob's advice to Arthur. Arthur looked at me, smiled, and said, "Darling, he just told you to go home and reinvent the wheel!"

In a way I suppose that's what I did, because my little kajal bullet turned out to be the right success formula. I sold thousands and thousands of them and their success enabled me to go on. Eighteen months after coming out with "Indian Eyes" I was at a trade show at the New York Coliseum and heard a visiting German executive announce in his talk to the American cosmetic industry that the latest fashion trend in Europe was the kohl/kajal eye makeup look and that "you Americans call it Indian Eyes." At that moment, I really knew I was launched and my reputation as a trendsetter established. I was on my way to realizing a dream. Suddenly, I had enough money to start creating what I'm gratified to know thousands of women of all ages and types consider the most exciting and innovative eye color collection in the cosmetic world. And always remembering Bob's advice, I chose my products with great care. They had to be original and of the best quality. And, most important, they had to make women *look* beautiful on the outside and *feel* beautiful on the inside.

It has only been six years since my cosmetic line was launched, but my dream of giving a top-quality line of eye makeup to women across this country and elsewhere throughout the world has progressed a long way. I am no stranger to the wonderful world of cosmetics and now you know I got my schooling working with real pros. I learned early in life about discipline, dedication, and devotion to my craft. I haven't changed. I've just added another dream. I have worked for my dreams and have made them a reality. When people made fun of me, even gently, I made that my spur. And I am proud of my achievement.

To all of the people who told me there was no way with only $7500 in capital that I could build a cosmetic business and try to buck the giants in their own territory, I say, "I did it." I have no doubt that they were right in their thinking. However, as my husband said, "Madeleine, you emulate the bumble bee." Not having any idea what he was talking about, I could see he was patiently waiting for me to ask why the parallel and so he explained. "According to the law of aerodynamics, the wing span of the bumble bee is too short for the weight of its body and the bee is therefore unable to fly. But because the bumble bee never studied aerodynamics, it continues to fly." I, too, hope to continue flying. Higher than ever.

MAKE EYES
WITH MADELEINE MONO

Anyone using the ideas expressed in this book should exercise caution in doing so. As the eyes are so sensitive, makeup should be carefully and gently applied. All products used should be checked first to make sure the contents are safe, especially if you have a particular allergic reaction.

The author and the publisher specifically disclaim liability for any loss or risk incurred by the use or application of any of the contents of this book.

1/ My Philosophy on Eye Makeup and Beauty

From women's eyes this doctrine I derive:
They sparkle still the right Promethean fire;
They are the books, the arts, the academes,
That show, contain and nourish all the world.
— WILLIAM SHAKESPEARE, *Love's Labour's Lost*

SHAKESPEARE ALSO SAID that the eyes are the windows of the soul. He must have been a very shrewd observer of the human race, for everything shows in the eyes—joy, pain, defeat, sorrow, love, adoration, and passion. Are they not our most precious instruments in conveying our emotions? I like to think of eyes as beautiful butterfly wings, and creating this effect with them should be pure pleasure, not a daily dose of medicine. Makeup is an art. And it *can* and *should* be a lifetime partner in expressing who you are.

If you have confidence in yourself, you can wear your makeup with great flair and panache. I was fortunate to gain my confidence early in life from the influence of my wonderfully beautiful mother, Lily Mono, who, even when the bombs were falling on wartime Britain, always emerged from the house impeccably made up and groomed—even if it was only to go to the air-raid shelters. Another woman who had a great influence on me at a very early age was Aida Foster, the owner and principal of the theatrical school I attended in London. Her makeup was always flawless and she had perfectly manicured hands. Whenever she left the room a lingering trail of fragrance that I can remember to this day stayed behind. My love for beauty, glamour, and perfume, engendered early, has grown through the years. And now, in my turn, I hope to have influenced my own daughters and helped train another generation of women in the art of being beautiful.

For me, the cornerstone of the art of makeup is the creative use of *eye color*. I am a great believer in experimenting with color, mixing and blending different shades together. If you are nervous about too much color, try adding a little at a time. But whatever you do, don't avoid it. If you never try, you'll never know. Remember, too, that when you see a vivid color in a cosmetic case it won't always transfer to the skin with the same intensity.

If you find you're a bit shy about using colors, try thinking about it the way I do—that is, think about how color affects you. You are affected by color in cosmetics just as you are affected by the sight of the sea or a clear blue sky. Sunshine makes you feel good and it brings warmth to the earth. A golden bronze eye shadow can stir up the same emotions. Try it one night and see for yourself. So don't be shy with color. Go with it. And come alive.

Have you ever heard this wonderful quote: "A beautiful woman alone is always in good company?" Beauty has many advantages and can help open many doors through life; if you have it, certainly you are blessed. Still, beauty alone is not enough. Being blessed with it, you are free to expand your horizons to encompass other interests and pursuits so that as you grow older your life is fulfilled. Beauty can also bring a good share of envy and jealousy. So be prepared for this. But remember that a truly beautiful woman is beautiful both inside and out and will never act in such a way as to make others feel inferior. Modesty is another aspect of beauty.

My beauty philosophy runs parallel to my living philosophy. A woman should color not only her face but also her life and the lives of those around her. For me, the application of makeup is a joy, a pleasurable pursuit, a lifetime hobby, and an adventure that I earnestly pray will never end. Even prior to starting my cosmetic business and continuing to this day, I have always had an insatiable desire to help others—be it the women in my family, close women friends, or any woman I come in contact with—learn how to beautify themselves and improve their looks. For I believe a plain woman *can* become attractive. A pretty woman *can* become beautiful. And a beauty may even become a legend. And to think all this can be achieved with the correct application of eye makeup! Because it *can* and this book will show you how.

I always tell my children that I will go to my grave glamorous. I hope I live up to that pledge, for glamour is my business. I live with it, work with it, surround myself with it, share it with millions of women around the world—enthusiastically. That's the key for me. *Enthusiasm.*

Enthusiasm is an important step up the ladder of success, money, power, and influence. If you never lose your enthusiasm for life, you can bring ideas in and entertain them royally for one of them may be the king (or in our case, the queen!).

That's what I did with my little magical kajal bullet. I brought a "new" look to the American woman that was really already centuries old. I nurtured it with my heart and soul and dreamed of bigger things. I am still dreaming, because beauty never has an ending. It is always a fresh start, a new idea—*a beginning.*

2/ Eye Equipment

The light of the body is the eye.
— NEW TESTAMENT

IMPROVING ON NATURE is like growing an English garden: one is always picking out the weeds. Learning how to be a beautiful woman is a life-long adventure. While you don't have to be born with any special talent to get great results, you do need patience, an eye for detail, the willingness to practice, and, above all, the *correct equipment* to do the job. Every artist has a few secret "tools of the trade," whether they are the exotic woods in a violin or the special leathers in dancing shoes. They're working assets that help make the magic happen. And making eyes more beautiful is no different. A worker is only as good as her tools, and proper eye makeup is an art that starts with having the right eye equipment. Each tool you use should be the finest in quality and the most comfortable for you to use. It doesn't matter whether your friend or mother or aunt says it works for her. It's *you* who must be satisfied because it's for you that the tool must perform.

Though many eye tools are faily standard in design there are slight differences to watch for. For example, the springiness of tweezers (degree of tension when squeezed) can make plucking fast and painless when the spring is loose or slow and tedious when the spring is stiff. The quality of cosmetic brushes can determine whether they blend or smear makeup. The sharpness of your eyebrow pencil point will result in strokes that are feathery and natural looking or heavy and fake.

My own cache of eye equipment has taken years to collect and I have some old favorites that I'll never part with. Even so, I'm constantly on the lookout for new items that will perform a special beauty trick better. But believe me, equipment variations exist, and though they might be subtle they're also crucial. So be aware of small details when selecting your collection. Take time and care when you shop. Sample when you can. Try before you buy.

Eye Equipment — The Mono Master List

Before we get to the actual ingredients of the master eye equipment list, let's divide it into two handy sections:

1. *Eye Maintenance Tools*—the more mechanical equipment designed for the maintenance and care of the eyes.
2. *Eye Cosmetic Tools*—those designed to beautify the eyes.

EYE MAINTENANCE TOOLS

TWEEZERS   Finding a really good pair of tweezers is not as easy as it seems. And since those that are sold in drugstores are packaged and sealed tighter than King Tut's tomb, you just can't try one out before you buy. If you're like most women, you'll probably wind up with a sizeable heap of "unusables" before you discover the right pair for you. And you *will* if you persist. Remember to invest in a good pair. You'll have them for a lifetime if you don't lose them, as I did recently. My tweezers were French, I'd had them for years, and somehow they got left behind while I was visiting my brother in London. I made a long distance call from New York City to be sure they were mailed off to me if found. On another occasion, I was in Florida and to my dismay I found I had left my tweezers at home. Iris, my best friend and the person I was staying with, said I could use hers—as long as I used them only in her bedroom!

Tweezers are absolutely indispensable to proper eye grooming and they do indeed become prized possessions. Investing in a good pair (which can cost anywhere from around $4 to $15) is worth every penny.

There are three basic types of tweezers. The difference is in the tip: *pointed, slanted* or *straight across*. I prefer the straight-tipped variety because they seem to have better "grab," but I suggest you try all three types to see which works best for you before deciding. (See pages 25–26 for "How to Tweeze.")

EYELASH CURLER   This is a "must" tool, a beauty gadget no woman should be without. An eyelash curler will do what mascara won't and the two should not be confused. Mascara *thickens;* a curler actually *curls* the lash. With just six seconds of gentle pressure, the rubber-tipped metal clamp curls the entire lash line in a dramatic upward sweep. Look for one with good quality rubber, as that part tends to dry out with age.

I have occasionally heard women complain that using an eyelash curler can be dangerous. This is simply not the case—if you use the curler properly. I have used an eyelash curler since I was fourteen years old and have never had even a minor mishap. My lashes are as long and thick now as they ever were. However, there are a few points to remember when using this tool:

 • Periodically check the rubber rim on the curler; if it seems to be drying out, lubricate it with baby oil.
 • Never use your curler if the rubber band is worn out or has fallen out as you may cut your lashes.
 • Curl your upper lashes only, never the lower ones.
 • Never use a curler on wet lashes or lashes that have mascara on them. In the former case, you'll simply be wasting your efforts, as wet lashes won't hold a curl; in the latter case, you run the risk of losing lashes that may stick to the curler and be pulled out from the lid when you remove the curler from your eye.

ROUND-ENDED SCISSORS   These small scissors are handy for trimming long or bushy brows. When you are ready for a trim, brush the eyebrow hairs down and snip off any excessively long stragglers in the line of the brow.

MAGNIFYING MIRROR   Certainly one of the most important makeup tools a woman can own and an absolute necessity for tweezing or applying eye makeup. Select one that is two-sided with both a plain and a magnifying mirror. I prefer triple-strength magnifying mirrors, as if I have a flaw, I want to see it first. On the other hand, some women prefer not to view their flaws so close up and opt for a double-strength mirror. Whatever suits you and feels most comfortable is what is best. Of course, eye grooming and makeup application in natural light is ideal, but when this is not possible, you may want to try a mirror with built-in lights that simulate day, office, and evening light. Remember, light has different qualities and affects color, balance, and tone. So don't ignore light conditions when working on your eyes.

COTTON BALLS These are indispensable for removing makeup and mascara, cleaning eye brushes and combs, and a host of other cosmetic "chores." Cotton balls are soft and gentle and are the *only* substance you should use to remove eye makeup. *Never* use tissues for eye clean-ups, as they are far too harsh on the delicate skin tissue around the eyes. Keep cotton balls in a closed container to be sure they are sanitary and bacteria-free.

Q-TIPS Great for cleaning up small spots where a wad of cotton can't reach—areas such as the corners of the eyes or under the bottom lashes.

EYE COSMETIC TOOLS

EYEBROW PENCIL An eyebow pencil is for *filling in* the sparse areas between your natural brow hairs. Proper penciling always looks natural and is best achieved by using a *soft* lead pencil with a very fine point and by making delicate, feathery strokes that simulate real brow hairs. A long eyebrow pencil is easier to handle than a short one and also gives you more control. Be sure to sharpen your pencil often to maintain the fine point.

Always use a pencil that is a shade *lighter* in color—never darker—than your own brows. I have found that one color in particular blends well for all eyebrows, whether they're light or medium brown, auburn, or even black. This color is a blend of pale blonde mixed with silver. Though it sounds rather strange, the combination gives a very natural look. Try it and be convinced!

Some women prefer to apply eyebrow pencil with an eyebrow brush, as this gives your brows a more natural look (see below). Either way is effective so long as you don't overdo it.

EYEBROW/EYELASH BRUSH   A small, stiff brush with either nylon or natural bristles is best for the daily care of your eyebrows. Most drugstores sell a variety of eyebrow brushes. To me, the handiest style is the brush designed with a small comb on the back. You can use the comb section to separate any lashes that stick together as you layer on mascara and the brush part to apply eyebrow pencil and whisk off any excess face powder that might cling to the brows. (A child's toothbrush is also fine for this purpose as its bristles are gentle yet firm.)

To apply color: Stroke the brush across your eyebrow pencil to "lift" some of the color and gently brush onto your eyebrow. Using the brush to apply eyebrow color eliminates the problem of getting too much color in one spot and not enough in another. It also distributes the pencil color uniformly through your natural brow hairs. Now, brush your eyebrows in an "up" motion to make sure they are all going in the same direction and to create a natural-looking, well-groomed eyebrow. Brushing the eyebrow is a finishing step many women forget, yet it takes only seconds and makes a tremendous difference in the final look of your eyes.

To groom brows: Use an eyebrow brush everyday to groom your brows, just as you use a hairbrush to keep your hair neat and in place. Your brows will really respond to the stimulation. Brush them up toward the hairline, then down, then back to their natural shape. Do this for about ten seconds. The change in direction gives brows a thorough workout. If you have wayward brows, regular brushing can train the brow hairs to grow in the direction you want them to.

To separate lashes: Use the comb on your brush to gently separate lashes that stick together from the mascara. This finishing touch, like eyebrow brushing, creates the illusion of extra fullness. Since you accessorize your eyes for drama, why not go all the way for memorable impact?

NOTE: **Never** *use a pin or needle to separate stuck-together lashes. This is extremely dangerous!*

MASCARA   This is an indispensable beauty aid for achieving thick, lovely-looking lashes. Regular mascara consists of water, oil, melting waxes, pigment (usually iron black), protein, fibers, and emulsifiers. There are several forms available:

Cake or block mascara is the original mascara and, in my view, still the best. It may take a bit longer to apply than other types of mascara because you have to first wet the brush, and then pass it to and fro over the block to work up a creamy consistency. To me, the extra time is well worth the effort as cake mascara does a beautiful job of thickening by building smooth, even layers.

Wand mascara is popular because it's fast and convenient and applies color evenly. Working women and busy wives and mothers prefer this quick, easy method to all others. Wand mascaras come with a variety of different applicators: *brushes, combs,* and *spiral screws.* The spiral brush is by far the most popular as it separates the lash hairs best. Some spirals are straight while others are contoured to the shape of the lash line. Experiment until you find the one you are most comfortable with.

Waterproof mascara was formulated for today's sports-minded women. It contains the same ingredients as regular mascara except that it has solvents instead of emulsifiers. Since it is waterproof, it is slightly more difficult to remove than other types of mascara. Also, waterproof formulas tend to dry out lash hairs; so after removing every trace of mascara, treat your eyelashes to a rich coating of castor oil or mineral oil before going to bed.

NOTE: *Some doctors now recommend that mascara should not be kept for longer than six or eight weeks because of possible bacterial contamination. Since your mascara—especially block types—may last considerably longer, take this caution into consideration when updating your cosmetic supply.*

CONCEALING CREAM OR HIDEAWAY   This is a basic for women who want professional-looking eye makeup because it is the foundation for everything else that follows. It hides shadows, circles, and discolorations and can also be used to conceal facial blemishes. The best concealing creams are those that contain lanolin for lubrication and talc, which creates a "holding" surface and acts as a base for eye shadows. Concealing cream usually comes in light, medium, or dark shades. For some women, one shade is all you'll ever need; other women, like me, need two shades, as your skin tone changes at different times of the year. During the winter months I use a light shade and in summer, a medium or dark shade, depending on my tan. When you buy a concealing cream, test it on your hand first to check for blending and consistency. If it's too greasy it will cause your makeup to smudge or run. If it's too dry it will tend to dry out the delicate skin tissues around the eyes.

To use: Apply moisturizer to the eye area. Dot concealer under the eye and over the entire lid right up to the brow line. Use a small, soft-tipped brush to blend concealer evenly.

EYE SHADOW   Eye shadows are available in colors as varied as an artist's palette and are either *matte* (non-shiny color) or *iridescent* (glossy, light-catching color). Matte and iridescent shadows can be used singly or together, depending on the effect you want to achieve. Matte shadows are ideal for daytime, as they are subtler and more understated than the dramatic, high-fashion iridescents, which are fabulous for evening.

Try mixing and matching matte and iridescent colors for the desired effect.

Loose iridescent powders come in dozens of beautiful hues, and, contrary to what you might suppose, are not difficult to work, with. They are the most creative eye cosmetic "tool" a woman can use.

To apply loose powder shadow: This type of eyeshadow should be applied with a narrow, soft-tipped angled brush. Dip the brush into the powder, gently blow off any excess from the brush (do this over a tissue so the powder doesn't get on your face or clothing), and brush on.

To apply pressed shadow: Pressed shadows can be applied with either a sponge applicator or an eye brush. To get a deeper, richer color with a pressed shadow, simply add a tiny drop of water before applying.

EYE COLOR PENCILS   I suppose I should mention that I am known as the original "Pencil Lady" because I believe that pencils are the most modern way of applying color to the face and I use them for almost every kind of makeup. Pencils are also small, portable, easy to use, and extremely convenient for any working woman. Best of all, they're economical—pencils cost only a few dollars each and will last for several months before you need to replace them.

Cosmetic pencils should all have soft leads for the gentle, non-pulling application the delicate eye skin deserves. How can you tell if a pencil lead is soft enough? Try the "Web Hand Test": Spread your thumb back and away from the rest of your fingers. The fleshy skin that spans the space between the thumb and the other fingers is called the "web," and though it feels soft, it's actually quite tough. Take your pencil and try marking the web with it. If the pencil color glides on easily you'll know it's soft enough to use on your eyes.

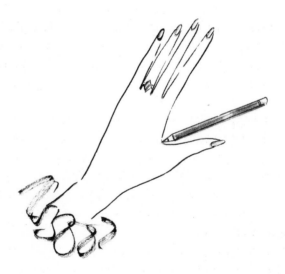

KAJAL: INSIDE EYE LINER PENCIL   This is the one cosmetic that will instantly change the look of your face. It certainly changed my life. Kajal is for lining the *inside* rim of the eye. It is unbeatable for bringing your eyes to their full potential and will make your eyes appear dramatically larger in seconds. Kajal will also make the whites of your eyes appear whiter for a totally feminine, provocative effect. Try it once and you'll be convinced.

Kajal is native to India and was originally used exclusively for medicinal purposes. Indian women applied it to their eyes to prevent infections and to their children's eyes to keep them cool and ward off evil spirits. The composition of the product (similar to kohl discussed below), consists of a carbon-black base mixed with oil, which acts as a connecting agent for the color pigment. The formula is very simple and has been handed down virtually unchanged from ancient times to today.

Kajal comes in the standard pencil form or in a small "bullet," which is the way it is used in India. In Far Eastern countries, kajal is sometimes applied with a little stick, but this is a very dangerous method of application as one slip can do a lot of harm. The pencil or bullet forms of kajal are the safest and most convenient to use.

Kohl: Outside Eye Liner Pencil Kajal is often mistakenly referred to as *kohl*. Of the two, kohl is perhaps the better known. But they are *not* the same thing and there is much confusion about this. Kohl is used to line *outside* (around) the eye and is not formulated for use inside the eye. (Even some major cosmetic companies do not understand this basic difference between kohl and kajal and sell them as though they were the same product designed for the same purpose. I have seen one large cosmetic company label "Kohl/Kajal" on a single pencil. This is impossible!)

Kohl comes from Egypt and, unlike kajal, came into existence purely as a cosmetic and not for medicinal reasons. Research tells us that the extremely vain Egyptian women colored their eyes and cheeks with products containing different kinds of pigment, the two most common being *malakite* (a green copper mineral) and *galena* (a dark gray lead mineral). Ancient kohl was made from the burned remains of special incense or almond shells. Present-day Egyptian kohl consists of carbon black produced by burning the wood of *Karthamus tinctorius* and is applied with a little stick fashioned of wood, ivory, or metal. The point is dipped in water, then into the kohl dust, and smudged around the outside of the eye for a striking effect.

The close analogies between kajal and kohl are due to the fact that all Middle and Far Eastern women felt the common need to use eye make-up with more or less medicinal effects. Trade with neighboring countries, which in ancient times was highly developed, probably allowed some products to be mixed and added to, which explains why kajal and kohl have similar characteristics today.

Kajal and kohl are available in several colors, black being the most dramatic for brunettes, redheads, and some blondes. Blue is especially good for blondes. If you have gray hair, you can choose almost any color kajal and kohl depending on your skin coloring and the intensity you require in your makeup. Some women look stunning with kajal and kohl, others can't take it at all. So you will have to be the judge in the final analysis.

NOTE: *Because kajal and kohl are used so close to the delicate interior of the eye, you need to take extra care when choosing and using these pencils. Some women find their eyes tear slightly when using kajal for the first time. This is not dangerous and the slight tearing will soon stop. However, you should be sure that the kajal you buy is formulated for safe use* inside *the eye, especially if you have sensitive eyes.*

HIGHLIGHTING PENCIL   This is a color pencil with iridescent pearl or gold pigments mixed in with the lead and it gives your eyes a soft, luminescent look. Highlighting pencils can be used with, on top of, or in place of eye shadow, and are wonderful for both day and night. They come in many beautiful colors and can transform your daytime makeup into nighttime makeup in just a stroke.

MATTE COLOR PENCIL   Matte pencils are available in a wide range of colors. They are perfect for the older, "crepy" eye because the soft lead glides onto the skin so easily. Matte pencils can be used in partnership with pressed shadows or loose powder shadows.

COSMETIC BRUSHES   These are the cosmetic tools you just can't have
enough of. I have at least twenty-five different kinds of makeup brushes
on my dressing table—twenty of them are eye brushes, many of which
I've had for thirty years!

I first learned to apply makeup with brushes when I was enrolled in a
theatrical school in London. All of us aspiring actresses were taught
how to apply our makeup, or grease paint as we then called it, with
long-handled brushes. There were two different types of brushes for applying eye shadow, another brush was for blushing, another for applying lipstick, and another, shaped like a crescent, for dumping off excess
face powder. I never stopped using my long-handled brushes. In fact,
when I began my cosmetic company my second product was a set of
these wonderfully useful brushes.

Professional makeup brushes blend well, give you excellent control
over color, and are hygienic. Brushes are economical, too, because they
use only what you need of the product and don't cause waste. Last, and
perhaps most important, brushes are not harsh on the delicate, easily
damaged eye skin.

The finest quality brushes made today are usually a mixture of pony and goat hair. (The days when brushes were made of sable have unfortunately come and gone as the price of this luxury product has become prohibitive.) Makeup brushes are an important cosmetic investment and, if you choose wisely, they will last a lifetime. So be sure to care for them—which means keeping them clean. Wash your makeup brushes every other week, or as needed, in a mild liquid detergent or an ordinary mild liquid soap.

Eye shadow brush: These usually come two ways: cut with an *angled end*, for easy application in the creases and folds of the eye, or cut with a *blunt end*, for blending, contouring, and smudging. If your budget is limited, buy two quality brushes: one for eye shadow powders and one for pencils. If you use more than one color, be sure to wipe off the brush on a tissue between applications.

Eye shadow sponge applicator: Sponge applicators should be mentioned here as they are particularly helpful when mixing water with pressed shadows. The sponge, however, is a better applicator of color than it is a blender. After using the sponge to apply the color, blend it in with a soft, angled brush.

PENCIL SHARPENER   If you use cosmetic pencils at all (and if you're like me, you have dozens!) you need a pencil sharpener, or perhaps two or three: one small sharpener for thin pencils and one larger size for your thick pencils. A pencil sharpener will keep the points of your pencils sharp and free from oil build-up that results when the pencil comes into contact with the lid and the lid oils get absorbed into the pencil's lead. Oil build-up occurs after repeated use and can prevent the color from coming through from the pencil onto your eye. It is best to buy a sharpener from a cosmetic counter as these sharpeners are specially made with very fine blades that do a precise, safe job of keeping your pencils in top repair.

NOTE: Never *sharpen your eye pencils with a knife. It is penny wise and pound foolish. Using a pencil sharpener will give better—and much safer—results.*

Though you may want to keep the number of eye shadows and colors in your beauty arsenal to a conservative count, most women—especially if they like to experiment with color and the interplay of makeup with their wardrobe (see Chapter 6)—build up a sizeable collection. The items on this master list are basics and make a real difference in making beautiful eyes. So, build your collection carefully and, once in place, keep it fresh and updated.

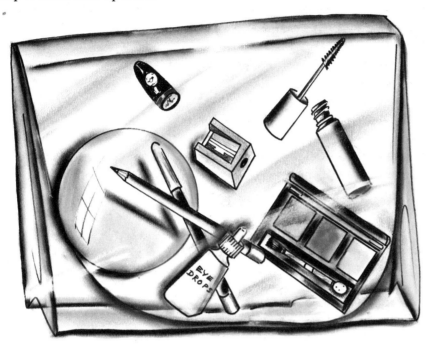

The Ready-for-Anything Carry Kit

With over half the female population in the work force, making eyes beautiful eventually translates into keeping eyes beautiful, especially as the day wears on and 5:00 P.M. draws closer. Most eye makeup, no matter how expensive or long lasting, needs refreshing and touching up. (For a "30-Second Touch-Up" that really works, see page 54.)

To be properly equipped to perform these instant touch-ups doesn't mean you have to carry along a fifty-pound sack. Keep your carry kit simple and the contents fresh and updated. This means a once-a-week "shake out": Empty your kit completely of its contents; check for spills; sharpen your pencils; clean your brushes; and replenish whatever is running low.

Your master collection of eye equipment is the cornerstone of your at-home beauty program. Your ready-for-anything carry kit is like insurance you can count on no matter where you are—even in an emergency or when traveling (although you really need to take more with you for extended trips). Both are essential for making eyes beautiful.

This is what you'll need for your basic kit:

Eyebrow pencil

Pencil sharpener (if your pencil breaks away from home you'll be in big trouble without one)

Mascara

Eye shadow (preferably a trio of colors that come in a purse-size case)

Kajal

Small mirror

Eye drops

Of course, in addition to the eye cosmetics listed here you'll need to include other makeup refreshers in your carry kit as well, such as lipstick, lipstick pencil, blusher, etc. Remember that eye makeup is not permanent and must not be forgotten after you put it on in the morning—after six or eight hours it's going to need some attention. When you invest this "touch-up" time, the attention your eyes will generate will more than make up for those extra minutes you so wisely spent.

3/ Eyebrows and Eyelashes

For where is any author in the world
Teaches such beauty as a woman's eye?
Learning is but an adjunct to ourself.
— WILLIAM SHAKESPEARE,
Love's Labour's Lost

ONE RAISED EYEBROW can trigger debate. One sudden flutter of the eyelashes can launch a love affair. Though they are small aspects of the overall face proportion, together brows and lashes have an impact so great they can and do transform beauty into legend. Consider Marlene Dietrich, Elizabeth Taylor, and the legions of other women who have turned on the world simply by the beauty of their eyes.

Eyebrows

Eyes and eyebrows are inseparable partners. Each needs the other for balance and harmony. I have seen the most beautifully made-up eyes absolutely ruined because the eyebrows started in the middle of the eye (a common mistake that is caused by incorrect plucking). Even worse is an otherwise stunning face totally naked of eyebrows because a woman went "plucking mad" and didn't know when to stop. Eyebrows frame and accessorize the eyes. They provide the finishing touch. That's why making sure they are the right shape, length, fullness, and color is an extremely important part of your program for making your eyes beautiful.

SHAPE: "MATCH THE ARCH"

The curve of the eyebrow is important for the balance of the entire face. Eyebrows should always follow the natural curve of your eyes, which is also to say that eyebrows should follow the natural curve of your lash line. How you create the proper shape for your eyebrows starts by knowing how to "Match the Arch."

1. Start with your lash line. Look at it carefully in the mirror and then trace its exact shape on a piece of paper.

2. Next, look at your eyebrow closely and draw its shape on the same piece of paper.

3. Now, compare the two arches by placing the eyebrow tracing above the lash line tracing. They should be mirror images of each other or at least fairly closely matched. If they are not, some corrective measures are in order.

If you're not particularly accurate at free-style drawing, have a friend do the tracings for you. Better yet, have your friend take a snapshot of your eyes and work with the print. Or, if all else fails, have a professional cosmetician shape your brows. Once you've established your proper brow line, you should be able to maintain it with ease.

LENGTH: THE "PENCIL TEST"

There are too many "eyebrow disasters" walking around simply because many women don't know where their brows should begin and end. Once you know the "stop and start" of them, it's an easy beauty procedure to trim or thin or lengthen your eyebrows to make them work better with your eye shape. The following "Pencil Test" is a simple, foolproof way to tell exactly where your eyebrows should begin and end.

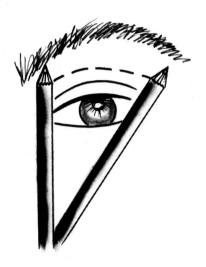

1. Hold a pencil vertically next to the base of your nose, with the tip of the pencil pointing up toward your forehead. The pencil forms a great "divide," a line that tells you where your eyebrow should *begin*. With the pencil in place, look straight into a mirror and see where your inside eyebrow hairs actually fall in relation to the pencil. If you find hairs on the inside side of the pencil, pluck them. It means your brows are starting too close to your nose. Now check the other side of the pencil. If there are not enough hairs to even touch the pencil, it indicates your brows are beginning too far from the nose. This area probably needs filling in with pencil.

2. Angle the same pencil outward about 45 degrees to the outside corner of your eye. This is where your eyebrow should *end*. If the brow goes beyond the pencil, trim the excess away. If, on the other hand, the end of your eyebrow doesn't reach the pencil, you'll need some filling in to lengthen the brow. Also, remember that the end of the brow should *never* be lower than the beginning point.

Once you've mastered this simple pencil trick you'll never have eyebrows off the mark—growing too closely together or ending short. They will be perfect from tip to tip. And that's exactly how you want them when you begin making up your eyes, because any imbalance will certainly affect your other features.

FULLNESS

How thick or thin should your eyebrows be? In general, your eyebrows should be pleasantly full but not bushy and never pencil thin. The ideal eyebrow is almost the same width all the way across, tapering slightly at the outer edge where it should fall away gently. (Never end brows abruptly!) And believe it or not, the ideal brow is almost always your own natural fullness. Many women alter their brows in an effort to follow the current fashion—even though fashion may dictate the "thin" brow only to switch in six months to a thicker look. To me this is a mistake. Brows are crucial to the balance and structure of your entire face and it's best not to tamper with their natural design.

The eyebrow should be one continuous curve that follows the natural curve of your lash line. It should not be pointed and peaked in the center nor should it thin noticeably from mid-brow to tip. The fullness of your brow is just as important as its shape. What you don't want is the Edith Piaf look—that pencil-thin brow which obviously has been drawn on because the real hairs were pruned away by an imprudent tweezer. However, some eyebrows *are* too full and bushy and some even meet in the center. These *do* need trimming—carefully. When you tweeze, be sure to trim away only those hairs obviously growing out of place.

HOW TO TWEEZE

For me, tweezing my eyebrows is like brushing my teeth: a daily ritual. Every woman should inspect her eyebrows in a magnifying mirror *daily*. If you do need to shape your eyebrows, remember that it's far easier to tweeze one or two stray hairs as they reappear, than to wait for an accumulated, unattractive build-up. *Never* tweeze when you're in a rush. It's a beauty procedure that calls for patience. Also, correct tweezing demands the correct equipment. Here's what you'll need:

Cotton balls
Witch hazel and alcohol
Tweezers
Eyebrow brush
Magnifying mirror

1. Remove all eye makeup first, then wipe your brow area with a cotton ball soaked with witch hazel to remove any excess oils or dirt.

2. Dip tweezer tips into alcohol to cleanse and sterilize. (Eyebrow follicles can easily become infected from unclean equipment, so be sure not to skip this step.)

3. Brush brows into a natural line with a slightly upward motion.

4. Work under the eyebrow first. Keep this area pristine clean and free of new growth. Those tiny hairs have a way of sprouting up fast and should be checked daily.

5. Don't tweeze above the brow unless you have obvious mavericks. Just pluck enough to keep the line looking tidy.

6. Never over-tweeze. Stop too soon rather than too late. Eyebrows react to excessive plucking by not growing back, so correcting tweezer slips may not be as easy as you think.

7. Wipe your eyebrows once more with cold witch hazel. This cleans and helps close pores.

Tweezing technique: Be sure to place your tweezer tip as close to the base of the hair as possible so you will pluck the *entire* hair shaft and root. All those unsightly root stubs are the result of plucking the eyebrow hair too far out toward the end, which causes the hair to break off before it's completely pulled.

Some eyebrows are oversensitive to tweezing. In order to minimize any discomfort, gently hold the skin taut with one hand while you pluck with the other. This will help eliminate any pain. If you have sensitive skin, tweeze your eyebrows in the evening so that any redness will disappear by the following morning. And remember, in order to keep your brows in top condition, check them for new growth every day.

What about waxing? Some women prefer waxing to tweezing, and it is certainly true that waxing gives a smooth finish that leaves your skin feeling silky and pampered. The trouble with waxing, however, is that you simply can't do it yourself (it's messy and one false move can remove an entire brow!). Also, once you've waxed you have to wait several days or even weeks for the growth to reappear, which looks unsightly. Much better to master the little tweezer yourself. It's cheaper, too.

What about electrolysis? This can be an expensive and time-consuming procedure as hairs are treated one at a time. Moreover, electrolysis is not reversible. If you do decide to use this method, you had better be absolutely certain what shape you want your brows to be, *forever.* Again, my advice is to become as professional as possible with your tweezers.

EYEBROW TIPS

The following tips will help you care for and maintain those well-groomed eyebrows:

• Generally, underplay the eyebrows.
• Follow the natural shape of the brow.
• Never apply color in heavy, solid lines. Rather, use light, fine, feathery strokes to simulate the natural eyebrow hairs. (See page 10.)
• Always work color vertically to create an upswept brow.
• Fill in pale brows.
• Eyebrows should always be a few shades lighter than your hair color, never darker. When they are darker they look artificial and have a tendency to distract from the beauty of your eyes.
• If your eyebrows are naturally darker than your hair, you might want to bleach them lighter yourself or have a professional do it for you. (You can go once, observe, and next time do it yourself.) Use a gentle facial hair bleach for a couple of minutes only. Over-bleaching will cause the hairs to break off, so be sure to read the directions that come with the bleach carefully.
• Never shave your eyebrows.
• If your brows are a bit flaky or scaly, lubricate them at night with a bit of vaseline, castor oil, or mineral oil.
• If your eyebrows won't stay in place, you can "fix" them by brushing on a bit of mustache wax or glycerine soap with a slightly moistened brow brush. This trick is particularly effective for women who like their brows brushed "straight up."

Eyelashes

Like eyebrows, eyelashes frame the eyes—but lashes connote more intimacy and allure. Even the loveliest brows cannot compare to long, silky lashes. One of my favorite stories about eyelashes concerns the great actress Joan Fontaine. David O. Selznick once sent Mont Westmore, the famous Hollywood makeup artist, the following memo about Joan Fontaine's screen test for Scarlett O'Hara in *Gone With the Wind:* "You have got those damnable false eyelashes on Miss Fontaine and they stick out like antlers on a freak elk. Further, there were no false eyelashes during the Civil War. Take them off!" Westmore's reply was brief: "Those lashes are Miss Fontaine's *own* lashes." After seeing the rushes, Selznick told Mont that he still didn't like her lashes and ordered him to trim them. Outraged, Westmore retorted, "If you want someone's natural and beautiful lashes trimmed, cut 'em yourself!"

Such a story proves the impact of sensational eyelashes. But even if you don't have the best eyelashes in the world to begin with, you *can* have beautiful lashes with just a little patience and know-how. First, make an honest evaluation of your lashes. Are they too thin, too sparse, too light in color? Are they thick and short or thick and long (the best possible combination)? Once you've analyzed them, you can overcome any shortcomings and play up the pluses with the right makeup.

EYELASH LENGTHENER

If you want to have long, luscious lashes instantly, without going the fake route, try this trick I learned in the theater:

First, curl your lashes with your eyelash curler following the guidelines on page 52. Next, take the tip of your forefinger and *lightly* dust your lashes with face powder or baby powder. The powder acts as a foundation and helps the mascara adhere. Then, apply your first coat of mascara. When it's dry, apply a second dusting of powder. Then a second coat of mascara. You'll be amazed at how thick and long and beautiful your natural lashes can look using this method. For the finishing touch, remember to use your eyelash comb to gently separate lashes that have stuck together.

EYELASH CARE

Lashes, like the hair on your head, need conditioning. On the average, an eyelash lives as long as 135 days or about four and a half months. During that time each dainty eyelash takes an incredible amount of abuse from water, sun, makeup, pollution, and lots more. To revitalize tired lashes or simply to make sure yours stay healthy, take the following measure:

Brush on a drop of castor oil or mineral oil at bedtime and let it soak in overnight. In the morning, use a cotton ball to gently remove any traces of lubricant, otherwise you'll have a hard time getting your eye makeup on properly. Mineral oils are inexpensive to use and the results are dramatic.

FALSE EYELASHES

My feeling about artificial lashes is to leave them on stage, under the lights. During my career in British theater, I wouldn't be seen during a performance without false eyelashes. After all, that last-row seat had to get a glimmer of my eyes, as they expressed the characters I played. But once in my dressing room, off came the false lashes and on went my "Mono look" eye makeup. Properly applied eye makeup is all you'll ever need to create beautiful eyes—with one exception. If you have lost your lashes from illness or accident you'll need false lashes to replace what will not grow back. Be sure to use only the finest-quality, natural-hair lashes.

False lashes can be applied in one of three ways: full strips, strip sections, or lash by lash. Experiment using sections or individual lashes for the most natural look. Of course, the right eye makeup used in conjunction with false eyelashes blends everything together for spectacular eyes.

One last word of caution: Applying lashes takes time, patience, and gentleness, but taking them off calls for even more of the same. Try putting a drop of baby oil on the lash adhesive to help loosen the lashes from the delicate skin area on the lid. Otherwise, you'll wind up pulling out some of your own precious lashes in the process.

EYELASH DYEING

Eyelash dyeing is something I do not recommend for most women. However, if you can't wear mascara because of an allergic reaction or an occupation where your makeup tends to melt off, dyeing your lashes is an alternative. For the best and safest results, dyeing should only be done by a professional cosmetician in a reputable beauty salon that is licensed to perform dyeing. If your lashes are dyed properly, the color should last for up to two months. My advice: Save your money—and perhaps your lashes—by investing in the finest quality mascara.

Every woman's eyebrows and eyelashes can be powerful beauty assets, given a little care, patience, and practice. The success formula is not secret; learning how is the magic ingredient. Once you've mastered the techniques for proper eyebrow and eyelash grooming, put them to work for you. Who knows? Your eyes just might be the cause of something very beautiful.

4/ Eye Types

Wine comes in at the mouth
And love comes in at the eye;
That's all we shall know for truth
Before we grow old and die
— WILLIAM BUTLER YEATS,
"A Drinking Song"

THE ALMOND-SHAPED EYE is the sign of great beauty. Just slip back a few thousand years and reflect on the impact Cleopatra made. Or think of modern times when Vivien Leigh and Greta Garbo mesmerized millions of movie fans with their eyes and inspired countless fantasies of love and romance. We can't all be famous beauties, but I've never seen a woman with ravishing eyes who *wasn't* beautiful—even if the rest of her features were ordinary. If your eye type doesn't fit that treasured outline, don't despair. Some the best-known models and stars have less than perfect features and still manage to turn those imperfections into the height of fashion that other women try to emulate.

When using makeup to enhance the natural beauty of your eyes and face, the key is to remember that your features must *relate* to each other. They are not isolated. An eyebrow is not an island apart from an eye any more than a nose is separate from a mouth. There are quick and easy corrective makeup tricks that can solve any proportion problem and restore balance and harmony to your face. But, before you correct, you have to know what the problems are.

EVALUATE FIRST! Let's do a little experiment. Without checking in a mirror, ask yourself what eye type you actually have. Think about it for a minute. Do you really know—*specifically?* I am constantly astounded to realize that many women—perhaps even most—don't really know the answer to this question! Over the years I have asked hundreds of women what kind of eyes they thought they had. And I never cease to be surprised by the answers. One response stands out vividly in my mind. This particular woman had large, very round eyes that were a clear blue. When I asked her what kind of eyes she thought she had, she answered, "Blue." That was it. She never even thought about their shape, their size. All she thought about was the color—and color alone does not establish eye type. When I told her that she had what I would call a "doe-eyed" look—a slightly startled, amazed look, upswept at the corners—her eyes twinkled with amusement and wonder. She was thrilled to make this "unique" discovery about herself. When I proceeded to give her some tips for how she could use color to further enhance her naturally attractive eyes, she literally went into raptures over her potential for beauty—potential she never realized she possessed.

I tell this story to many women I meet because it is a typical one and it illustrates a crucial point: In order to evaluate what eye type you have, rather than focus on a single element like color, analyze *all* the elements that collectively make your eyes uniquely yours.

EYE ELEMENTS Look in the mirror and try to determine exactly what your eyes are like. Remember, an eye type is a collection of many parts: the *iris,* the color area around the pupil, whose size makes eyes seem larger or small; the *length of the eyelid,* which can extend so far down that it narrows the eye or can be so minimal you scarcely see it; the *angle of the brow bone,* which determines the natural arch over the eye; the positioning of the *eyes relative to the eyebrows,* which can cause a too-narrow or too-wide look; the positioning of the *eyes relative to the nose* (too far from the nose gives you a wide-eyed look, while eyes set too closely to the nose cause a pinched look); the *depth and definition of the crease in the lid;* and so on.

Analyze each of these components critically and objectively. Some of your eye features are bound to be closer to perfection than others. Keep in mind that no woman was born with absolutely perfect eyes or the perfect face; even the most beautiful women have flaws, though they may not be immediately obvious to others. All these components come together to determine what eye type you have. Each works with the others to give expression and balance to the face.

CORRECTING FLAWS AND BEAUTIFYING PROBLEM SPOTS   Makeup can enhance these areas and, in most instances, even correct imbalance and proportion problems. For example, the *eyebrows*, when properly shaped and penciled, give expression and frame the eyes. *Eye shadow* gives the eyes shape, depth, color, and shine. *Kajal* (inside eye liner) defines the eyes and opens up the entire eye area. *Mascara* gives contrast, length, and fullness to lashes, which in turn complete your eyes and give them a well-groomed, dramatic look.

When you understand what each eye element is and what it does, you'll be better able to use it, maximize it, make it work in harmony with the rest of your face. Now, let's look closely at each eye type and explain how you can use some simple eye makeup techniques to correct any imbalance or disproportion and bring out the absolute best of your beautiful eyes.

Eye Types

ALMOND EYES

The almond eye is the one-hundred-percent perfect eye, and its upswept lift at the outer corner is what most women strive to achieve through the art of eye makeup. The way the shape, angle, and proportion of this extraordinary eye type come together always reminds me of a great tapestry. Lucky you if you were endowed with this gift at birth, for almond eyes do not require any special makeup corrections. However, I'm a firm believer in improving on nature, so to make the most of this eye type I like to emphasize the upswing of the corners even further.

Technique 1: Brush on deep-toned eye shadow or even black kohl in a lopsided triangle, so that the triangle peaks an equal distance between the end of the brow and the lower lash line. This area can and, especially at night, should be darkened more than the rest of the eye area and used as a base for your other eye shadows. The effect is added depth and drama and absolutely knock-out feminine eyes.

Technique 2: For less dramatic, more natural-looking almond eyes, this makeup trick will subtly emphasize your eyes without exaggerating their shape. Blend a neutral-tone eye shadow (soft pink, peach, or beige) on the brow bone. Apply a slightly deeper-toned shadow (in the same color family) to the eyelid. Line the upper and lower inside eye rims with brown, blue, or black kajal.

ROUND EYES

Round eyes can be very attractive so long as they are not made up to look too doll-like. When you apply eye shadow, keep in mind that what you are trying to achieve is the illusion of extra depth to make your eyes seem larger and more oval and to bring them into balance with the rest of your features:

Technique: Start at the inside corner of the eye. Using a deep-toned eye shadow in any color, blend the color in an upward angle toward the outer edge of the brow. Concentrate the color in the corner and fade it out as you work up toward the brow. Apply shading under the lower lid, again extending the line up and outward and blending it into the color above.

When making up the round eye, remember that the entire upper lid needs subtle shading, which you can do by extending the shading from the corner of the eye outward and upward to the brow line. You can shade in any of several colors, depending on what other eye shadow colors you will be using. There are so many colors available for making up your eyes that it's a shame to stick to just browns or taupes. Olive green or copper, for example, provide an interesting and attractive change of pace. I am forever trying new color combinations as I find I get bored when my eyes look the same all the time. Sometimes I will get a good reaction from people around me, sometimes not so good. But I believe that change is helpful and adds sparkle—especially when you're in a rut. When making up the round eye, remember also to shade under the lower lid, being sure to bring the line upward rather than straight out.

SMALL EYES

Small eyes are eyes that have the iris, or color area, proportionally smaller than the whites of the eyes. One of my closest friends in England, an actress who often appears on television in the United States, has eyes that are actually quite small, but unless you were to look at them with a triple-strength mirror you would never suspect it, so artfully has she learned to make the most of what are certainly less-than-perfect eyes. To make small eyes appear larger, the trick is to give them more importance.

Technique 1: Use a fairly light shadow on the lid directly above the lashes. Then apply a darker shadow near the crease. Do not take the color too far toward the inner corner as this will narrow your eyes more. When applying shadow at the sides, use your brush to blend one color into the other to create a subtle look.

Technique 2: Line the inside rims of the eyes with white liner pencil, instead of black, blue, or brown kajal. Blend a soft, neutral-colored pencil (soft gray, brown, or taupe) under the lower lash area to create a wide-eyed, open look. Finish your makeup with two or three coats of mascara and you'll be amazed at how dramatically larger your eyes will appear.

NARROW EYES

Women who have narrow eyes, where only a part of the eye shows through the lashes, need to use makeup to open up their eyes. The following three-step technique will help you do just that.

Step 1: Brush on a light-toned highlighter shadow (white-gold or pink-gold) in either matte (for day) or iridescent (for night), blending it from the center of the lid to the top of the brow bone and making sure the entire brow bone is covered.

Step 2: Using a medium-toned shadow that coordinates with the highlight color, start at the inside corner of the lid and blend up toward the brow, shading and fading out the color as you reach the center of the lid. Be sure you don't go beyond that point.

Step 3: Starting at the outside corner of the eye, use a deep-toned shadow in the same color family to blend and shade up toward the brow. Concentrate the color at the outside corner of the lid, fading it as you work outward.

If you have narrow eyes, curl your lashes and very carefully wing a little black or blue kajal eye liner on the outer ends of your eyes. It is also helpful for women with this eye type to *slightly* arch the eyebrows by tweezing or penciling them, thereby leaving a defined shape in which to apply color above the eyelid. *If you have blue eyes,* outline your eyes with a deep blue kohl, kajal, or eye liner, but avoid harsh lines. The line must be underplayed by "smudging" rather than overplayed. *If you have brown eyes,* use a brown kohl, kajal, or eye liner, being sure to keep a subtle hand as you apply. (Using a fine brush to apply kohl is a very professional way of achieving a subtle look.) Cotton swabs are excellent for achieving the "smudged" look, which is really not smudged at all, just skillfully applied. Experiment to find the technique that you are most comfortable with. If one method doesn't work, try another.

WIDE-SET EYES

Wide-set eyes are eyes that are located a bit too far from the bridge of the nose. Such eyes can be striking but they can also appear lost from the rest of your face, thereby creating an imbalance. In order to bring them back into partnership with your features and achieve a more uniform look, you need to minimize the space that separates them.

Technique: Shade between your eyes and the bridge of your nose with a powder that is slightly darker than your skin tone, but not so dark that it will be noticeable. (Most models and makeup artists do this as a matter of course.) Take a small blusher brush and gently stroke the powder down the side of the nose. A contour powder works best. Again, practice with your magnifying mirror until you get it right. Next, use a highlighter under the outside edge of the eyebrow. Then shade the crease line, especially toward the inside corner of the eye near the nose, and finish the look by using a pale or light shadow on the outer corner of the eye.

DEEP-SET EYES

Some eyes are sunken far enough into the face that you fail to realize their potential drama. If you have deep-set eyes you need to bring them forward.

Technique: Brush a pale shadow over the entire lid area, ending it just above the hollow of the crease. Use a soft brown or taupe shadow to shade the area from the brow bone to the brow. Emphasize the area just over the natural crease with smudged pencil or shadow in brown, taupe, or light gray.

CLOSE-SET EYES

Close-set eyes are fairly common. In fact, many more women have eyes set too closely together than eyes spaced too far apart. To correct this imbalance you need to shift attention to the outer part of the eye.

 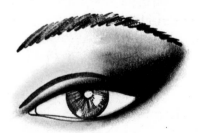

Technique: Brush highlighter on the inside corner of your eye. A white primer is fabulous for this purpose. Blend it well into the side of the nose. The light color creates the illusion of more distance between the eyes. Now, apply a dark-toned shadow on the outside third of the brow bone to give an upward sweep. Layer on extra mascara in a sweeping outward motion.

If your eyebrows are also too close together, try plucking them a little at their beginning near the nose to create a greater sense of distance between them. (But please don't go plucking mad! Check the "Pencil Test" on page 23 before you begin pruning.)

DROOPING EYES

Drooping eyes are eyes where the outer corners of the eye actually take a downward dip, giving your face a somewhat sad expression. What you need to do is lift the sagging corners.

Technique: Start by reshaping and raising the outer part of the eyebrow. Pluck any stray hairs that might be creeping down toward your eye (the outer end of your eyebrow should never be lower than its beginning point). Brush on shadow from the inside corner of the eye in an upward and outward direction almost to the brow line. Don't shade the outer edge of the lid where the eye begins to droop. The trick here is to create another crease line that is higher than your own by shading it with a taupe or brown eye shadow. Be sure to curl your lashes—you'll be delighted at the difference it makes. Finish with at least three coats of mascara.

PROTRUDING EYES

The problem with protruding eyes is usually eyelids that are too pronounced. The object here is to minimize the lids.

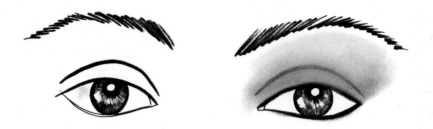

Technique: Cover the entire lid with a medium or deep tone of matte eye shadow. Blend the shadow right up into the lower brow area. Brush on a soft pink tone on the underbrow. Eye liner as well as kajal applied on the inside of the lid will also help de-emphasize a prominent lid. Be sure to curl your eyelashes. Layer on mascara, concentrating it on the center portion of the lid.

ORIENTAL EYES

This is the most exotic eye type, but one that requires special makeup tricks to bring out its best. The Oriental eye is characterized by a very minimal lid which may protrude or seem to disappear completely. The following makeup techniques will add depth and shape to this eye:

Technique: Brush a light-toned matte eye shadow all over the eye area. Then blend a medium-toned shadow on the inner corner of the eye, concentrating the color closest to the bridge of the nose and blending toward the center of the eye until the shadow fades away. This will bring the nose up and out. Brush a slightly darker shade of shadow on the outer corner of the eye, again keeping the color concentrated as close to the lid as possible. Blend from the outer corner of the lid to the outer edge of the eyebrow, then toward the nose. This adds depth and balances out the entire eye.

Apply liner, using a fine eye liner brush, as close to the base of the lashes as you can. This will give the appearance of a much thicker lash line and will add more dimension to the eye. Line both the upper and lower inside rims of the eye with black, brown or blue kajal to make the whites of your eyes appear even whiter. Line the area below the outside of the lower lashes with a soft, natural shade of kohl, blending most of it away to leave just a slight hint of color. Follow with mascara. This makeup technique will give any Oriental eye a soft, sultry, deep-set look.

BLACK EYES

I've never seen a black woman who didn't have striking eyes. The white of the eye is a fabulous contrast to the rich texture of black skin. No matter how beautiful, a black woman's eyes can still have certain proportion problems—especially when the lid is overpowered by a too prominent brow line.

Technique: To minimize the brow area, use a darker shadow on the outer half of the lid. Be sure to blend it in well. Use a bright color eye shadow on the center of the lid and take it right up under the brow. Use kajal to line inside the upper and lower rims of your eye. Then line the under lid of the eye with a bright, high-fashion color such as mauve or bright blue. This rim of color should be of medium width—not too thin—as you really want to show off that slash of color. Finish with three coats of black mascara. Try tipping the edges of your lashes with blue or purple for a stunning evening effect. No woman can wear color better than a black woman, so take advantage of your natural potential.

DIFFERENT-SIZED EYES

Unless you are a Greek goddess, it is almost certain that the two sides of your face are slightly different from each other. Most of the time this difference is barely noticeable, but some women are bothered by what they feel is an "out of kilter" look, no matter how imperceptible it may be to others. Here's what you can do to correct any such imbalance.

Technique: Study your face in the mirror and locate exactly where the imbalance is. Use shading color to even the proportions of your eyes. Always follow the simple corrective contouring formula: *dark pushes back, light brings forward.* For example, those areas that you want to minimize, like the brow or lid, should be shaded with dark tones. Those areas you want to accentuate and bring out should be toned with a light shading color. Remember, there's no one way to correct a flaw. Just keep practicing until the balance looks right.

AGING EYES

Not enough is said or done for aging eyes. I feel very strongly about this, simply because sooner or later, we're all going to get them!

The biggest trouble spots for aging eyes are sagging brows, wrinkles, and crow's-feet—all acquired from a lifetime of laughing, crying, eye-straining, whatever—though you are bound to think of plenty of other imperfections besides. Of course, many women resort to plastic surgery to correct these flaws, but if you're like me—a devout coward—powder and paint will have to suffice. Keep in mind that the objective in making up this eye is to uplift and recede the whole area from the lashes to the brow.

Technique: Use a medium dark shadow but only in a matte shade. Never use a bright, pale, or iridescent shadow as this will only attract attention to the problem area. Dab a tiny bit of highlighter just under the center of the brow to create an illusion of "lift." Also, try lining the inside rims of your lids with kajal, but be sure you line only from the middle to the outer corner of the lid, as this will reduce the downward droop. A subtle wing of eye liner or kajal in the outer corner of the eye will also create an illusion of "instant uplift," Finish with mascara.

A good tip to remember, especially if you feel a bit awkward or nervous about applying eye makeup, is to put on your foundation, powder, and blusher *after* you've finished making up your eyes. This way you can be sure to clean away any smudges or slips neatly, and without messing your eye makeup.

The thirteen eye types just reviewed cover all the bases. However, women have combination eye types—such as small eyes with drooping brows or protruding eyes with puff lids. If you are one of these women, don't fret. The same corrective measures apply. What counts is that you care enough to look and evaluate what nature has given you and then try to improve on it. Be willing to experiment and to welcome change. Don't get "stuck" with one safe look. You'll surprise yourself and everyone else around you when you learn to use eye makeup creatively, imaginatively, and with professional flair. And when you do, you'll discover that eye makeup is much more than powder and paint. It's magic!

5/ The 5-Minute Mistake-Proof Daytime Eye Makeup

There are no ugly women, only lazy ones.
— HELENA RUBENSTEIN

I DEVELOPED THIS FIVE-MINUTE, foolproof eye makeup system over the course of many years in the cosmetic business and through lots of trial and error. They say one learns from one's mistakes, and the following plan has been pared down to include only those steps essential to instant eye beauty. Certainly there are many other techniques and personal tricks you can add, but my five-minute method is terrific for basic daytime wear. It will help you look lovely (in as short a time as it takes you to boil an egg) for the office, the classroom, shopping, lunching, for whatever you do between the hours of nine and five when you want your eyes to look their best.

DAYLIGHT IS DIFFERENT   Why the distinction between eye makeup for daytime and other times? First, light is a very important factor in creating perfect makeup. Light affects *color*, *balance*, and *tone* and various light conditions have considerably different effects on color. Thus daylight has a different *quality* from evening light. In natural light, for example, you are better off using less eye color rather than more, as compared to evening when the dimmer, softer light seems to "blot up" color.

Your eyes also express different moods and communicate different feelings at different times of the day. You wouldn't want to look as dramatic or exotic at a business meeting as you would over a romantic

cocktail rendezvous. In fact, if you are a business executive, your associates may find it hard to take you seriously if you present budget figures while looking out from under elaborately made-up, seductive eyes. Of course, this isn't to say that you can't wear any eye makeup or that it must be so subtle that it looks washed out. Not at all! Eye makeup can still make a terrific impact if it's done quietly and with taste—through the use of more natural and subtle color, contouring, and highlighting. (See Chapter 6 for more on color.)

PRACTICE MAKES PERFECT! Before you begin my five-minute method, make the decision to practice the procedure step-by-step at home whenever you have the time. You'll be amazed at how quickly you become adept at *applying* color accurately, *contouring* the eye both above and below, and *layering* mascara correctly. Remember, too, shading and blending is the all-important key when it comes to applying eye makeup. It's what separates the beginners from the pros. Learn to blend colors well. Properly applied eye makeup never shows noticeable bands of color but is a continuous flow of one color into the other.

HOW TO WORK Eye makeup should always be applied *step by step.* Many women prefer to work on one eye at a time, finishing the first eye completely before starting on the other. Since making eyes is an extremely personal matter, there's no way that works for everyone. How you apply your makeup depends on how you prefer to work. It's the result that counts. What is natural and easy for you may not be for someone else. My own preference is to work step by step alternating from one eye to the other, as I have found this gives my eye makeup better balance. You may feel the same. If you're not sure, try working both ways until you find the method that's best for you.

Also, there are two schools of thought regarding *when* to apply eye makeup. I prefer to apply my eye makeup *after* all my other face make-up is in place. But many women reverse this process and apply their eye makeup first, before foundation and blush. Applying eye makeup first is a good idea if you're not accustomed to using eye cosmetics regularly and feel you're apt to mess your facial makeup with eye shadow and mascara smudges.

CORRECTING MISTAKES   Have a generous supply of cotton-tip swabs handy for cleaning up slips and smears as you practice your eye makeup. Cotton swabs are softer to use than tissues and much more hygienic than your fingers.

Now let's begin to watch the magic happen.

5-Minute Mistake-Proof Daytime Eye Makeup*

Before you apply any eye makeup your face should be thoroughly cleansed. Double-check to make sure you have removed all traces of yesterday's mascara. Pat on your regular moisturizer. Now you're ready to begin.

FRAME

Eyebrows frame the eyes, so your first step is to *groom your eyebrows.* However, different schools of thought exist about when you should apply pencil to your brows. Some women prefer putting pencil on first before any other eye makeup while others leave it to last. I prefer to do it first, as the finished brow becomes a handy guide to follow when I apply eye shadow. In either case, you should always tidy your brow line before making up your eyes. (If you're not sure how to tweeze or where your eyebrows should begin and end, review Chapter 3.)

*Please refer to the color insert for step-by-step illustrations of the techniques that follow.

1. Tweeze away any excess hairs so that your brow is clean and neat.

2. To prepare your brows for penciling, brush them into their natural arch with an eyebrow brush. Always brush in an up and outward direction. Never pencil your brows before you have brushed them as brushing helps show up the sparse areas. Now you're ready to pencil.

3. Using a well-sharpened eyebrow pencil that is one shade *lighter* than your natural brow color, make delicate, feathery strokes that simulate real eyebrow hairs to form a perfect arch. (Be sure your pencil is sharp. A dull pencil will never give a clean, natural look.)

Never darken your brows so they become too obvious or dominate your eyes and the rest of your face. Eyebrows should be a shade or two lighter than your hair color. Use the pencil sparingly and fill in *only* those areas that need it. Overdoing it can be disastrous, as we know if you've ever seen a brunette who uses lots of jet-black eyebrow pencil. Darkening your brows will not make you look more youthful nor will it draw attention to your eyes; it will, however, ruin the beauty and impact of the rest of your eye makeup. When it comes to eyebrow pencil less is definitely better than more.

4. Brush your brows upward with an eyebrow brush (a baby's toothbrush is perfect) to smooth all the hairs and make sure they're all going in the same direction. Brushing creates the elegant uplift that all eyes need.

CONCEAL

If you are like most women, you will need to hide or block out shadows, circles, or discolorations around your eyes. Now is the time to apply a concealing cream. Select one that blends well with your skin tone. Concealing cream usually comes in light, medium, and dark shades. If you can't find one that exactly matches your skin tone, use a concealer that is slightly lighter than your skin tone—never darker.

The quality and proper application of your concealing cream is very important as it acts as an adhesive for the layers of eye shadow that follow. The best concealing creams are those that are formulated with lanolin and talc. The lanolin moisturizes the eye area and the talc absorbs the oil—the culprit that causes your eye shadow to crease as the day wears on. Concealing cream creates a perfect canvas for your eye makeup.

   1. Place little dots of the cream under and around the eye area with a small blusher brush made of soft bristle.
   2. Gently blend in with your fingers until there are no tell-tale lines.

Now you are ready to set your "canvas" with powder.

POWDER

Powder is an important step in the proper application of eye make-up—one that many women neglect. Powder sets your makeup; keeps your skin from absorbing the makeup; absorbs oils and prevents the oil in your skin from changing the color of your foundation; tones down shine; and is an extra layer of protection for your skin against air pollution, sun, etc. Don't forget to use powder!

   1. Place a small amount of loose translucent or light-colored powder in the palm of your hand.
   2. Gently and evenly distribute a thin layer of powder over the entire eye area with a swansdown puff, cotton ball, or large powder brush. Remove any excess powder by brushing downward.

COLOR

Now you're ready to shape, define, and give depth to your eyes with color. All eye shadow should be uplifting and liberating to the eyes, never drab and somber. The following rules should be remembered whenever you apply color to your eyes.

     1. Always coordinate the colors of your shadow with your complexion and clothes and contrast them to your natural eye color.

     2. You need to use more than one color to achieve a beautiful effect. The correct technique for applying eye colors requires a minimum of *three* shadow colors: *a light and medium tone for contouring plus a light shade for highlighting.* When you're selecting shadow colors, look for those that come prepackaged with three coordinating shades.

Many women are accustomed to using only one or at most two colors of eye shadow, and, at first, three colors may sound a little too colorful or complicated. I assure you it is not. If you restrict yourself to one or two colors, you'll just be painting away and achieving nothing—no shape, depth, or definition. And, after all, that's what eye shadow is all about. Why not try it my way? You'll love the results. (For more on how to coordinate and use eye makeup color, see Chapter 6.)

     3. It's best to apply shadow with an angled eye shadow brush that is specially designed to fit the contours of the eye. A brush gives you superior control and can be used to apply more than one shadow, since the hair bristles don't absorb color. Simply wipe the bristles off on a tissue each time you change color.

   Color does a lot more than "dress" the eye. Correctly applied, color will open up your eyes as well as give them interesting depth and shape. Applying color is a two-step process of *contouring* and *highlighting.*

CONTOURING Contouring with color will define the eyes and give them greater depth and better shape. There is one color code to remember: *light colors will bring out the eyes, dark colors will push them back.* With this in mind:

     1. Shade the entire brow area and the lid with a light shadow color. This will draw attention to the parts of the eyes that you would like to stand out.

     2. Brush on a medium-tone shadow color (deeper than the color

you just used) in the classic V shape, with the V lying on its side. Start the V at the center of the crease (this is the open end of the V shape, not the pointed end). Work the color out and down at an angle until you reach the outside corner of the lid. Be sure not to extend the color beyond the end of your lash line; otherwise your eye will be "dragged down" by the color and you'll wind up with a droopy look rather than the uplifted look the V is intended to create. Look slightly down so that you can see your full lid more easily and continue to apply color, working along the base of the lash line back to the center of the lid. This completes the V shape.

3. Blend the V. Wipe your brush and carefully blend the medium-tone shadow used to make the V into the lighter shadow underneath. Start at the outside corner and work in toward the center. The shading should be darkest at the outside corner of the lid, fading gradually as it comes to the center and inner portion of the lid.

HIGHLIGHTING Highlighting with color comes next. Highlight color has a distinct purpose, quite different from that of the colors you use to contour and shade. Highlighters are intended to *open up the eye.* They should always be in the same color family as your eye shadow, but at least three shades *lighter* than your contouring shadow color.

1. Dot the highligher up the center of the lid and under the brow.

2. Blend in, working the highlighter into the color so that the shades subtly flow into each other with no great distinction between colors.

NOTE: *There are two cases when you should* not *use highlighter: if you have a very "crepy" wrinkled lid area or deep-set eyes with a protruding brow bone. In these instances highlighter will only further emphasize the flaws.*

LINE

Liner will further define, balance, and add shape to your eyes and is indispensable for a look that is polished and beautiful. Select a liner in a color that is complimentary to the shades of your eye shadow.

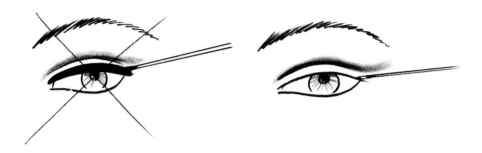

1. Stroke a finely pointed cosmetic brush (with just a small amount of liner clinging to the brush) across the top lash line and under the lower lashes. The line should be as thin and as close to your lashes as you can make it so it does not look obvious.

2. Line to the end of the lash line or wing the line out about an eighth inch beyond the outer corner of the eye for a subtler look.

RIM

Rimming the eyes with inside liner or kajal does far more than create immediate drama. It whitens the whites of the eyes; brings out your own eye color; outlines and defines the eye like nothing else will; and even creates the illusion that your lashes are longer than they really are.

1. Gently pull back your upper lid until you can see the rim of flesh just underneath your eyelashes. Hold the lid in this position while looking into the mirror.

2. Place the kajal pencil on the exposed rim and *gently* line it with color all the way from the inside corner across to the outside corner. Be sure the entire rim is darkened.

3. Repeat on the inside of the lower lid.

Kajal comes in pencil form and in several colors. Keep your pencil in good shape with regular sharpening, although it should never be too sharp, as it will feel uncomfortable on your lids. Kajal also comes in a small, bullet-shaped applicator which doesn't require sharpening. Black kajal is certainly the most striking color, but there are browns and wonderful blues that look especially well on fair-skinned blondes.

It takes a bit of practice to learn to apply kajal correctly and your eyes may feel sensitive to it at first. But once you get used to the feeling, applying kajal will become second nature and you won't want to make up your eyes without it.

LASHES

Beautiful lashes are the crowning glory of your eye makeup, and to get them you're going to *curl* and *mascara*.

CURL Curling your lashes with an eyelash curler is extremely easy to do and a must for a flattering look. Always curl lashes *before* applying mascara or you run the risk of damaging the lash hairs. Also, the curl won't take as well.

1. Hold the curved wand to the base of your upper lash line and gently squeeze it closed. Hold for six seconds.

2. If you missed some lashes, repeat the process. Do not curl the lower lashes.

MASCARA Whether you use cake-type or the more popular wand mascara, the application process is the same. Just remember, you can never apply too much mascara as long as you apply it in *thin* layers.

1. Using a brush applicator (it separates the hairs better) and starting with the top lashes, look slightly downward and layer on a thin

coat of mascara to the top of your lashes. Work from the root out to the tips and try to cover each individual hair on your lash line.

2. Open your eye and mascara the underside of the lashes. Turn the wand slowly as you apply.

3. Now layer on mascara to the upper surface of the bottom lashes. (Never apply mascara to the under surface of your bottom lashes; it looks overdone and will undoubtedly smear your face.)

4. Repeat this process once more. By layering on the mascara in this fashion, it will dry by the time you apply the second coat.

5. After your mascara has been applied and is dry, finish by brushing your lashes with an eyelash brush or comb to separate any hairs that stick together and to give your lashes a sweeping, uplifted look.

FINISHED! Check your watch. If it took more than five minutes you still need practice. Chances are your first few tries with this seven-step system may take a little longer, but you'll improve with each application as you become more skilled. Practice is what makes the difference between mediocre and professional-looking eye makeup.

How to Remove Eye Makeup

Your eye area is very delicate and must be treated with great care, so it's worth spending a little extra time to remove your eye makeup properly. Here's how:

Apply a fragrance-free, non-oily liquid eye makeup remover to a soft cotton ball and gently wipe off your eye makeup. Work from the inner corner of the eye toward the outer corner. Repeat, changing cotton as needed, until there is no trace of makeup left on your cotton ball. Now repeat with the other eye. Always use a fresh cotton ball when you switch to your other eye so you won't run the risk of transferring bacteria from one eye to the other.

NOTE: *I prefer fragrance-free, non-oily liquid eye makeup removers but there are other products which are equally effective, such as pads impregnated with oil or even eye makeup remover gels. Some women like to use mineral oil, petroleum jelly, or cleansing cream to remove eye makeup. This is your choice. My own feeling is that it's best to use a product specially formulated to do the job because it will usually be extra gentle on the skin.*

30-SECOND TOUCH-UP

As the day wears on, your eye makeup will probably begin to wear off or smudge. The following touch-up will restore your eyes to their full beauty:

• Dab on a bit of concealing cream under your eyes to hide any after-five circles. Then dust the area lightly with face powder.

• Smooth an angled eye shadow brush over your eye crease to eliminate smudges or cracks in your shadow or contour shading. If you've used a good quality shadow, you probably won't need to apply another coat of color.

• Your highlighter, however, will probably have disappeared completely. Stroke on a bit more just under the brow with your eye shadow brush.

• Gently re-rim the inside lids of the eyes, both top and bottom, with kajal.

• If you are going to dinner or a party you can achieve a stunning transformation instantly by stroking on an iridescent pencil or eye shadow. Pure, iridescent colors are delicate and will immediately transform classic daytime eyes into sexy nighttime eyes.

What About Night Creams?

Your eyes should be completely clean before you go to bed. As far as night eye creams are concerned, unless they are extremely light and sheer—the kind that disappear completely into the surrounding eye area—my feeling is that they do more harm than good, and you are likely to wake up in the morning with puffy eyes. Better to apply eye cream or a very thin coat of vitamin E oil to your lashes in the morning. Leave it on for thirty minutes (if time allows) or at least while you have your morning coffee and read the paper. Gently pat off the excess with a cotton pad before applying your makeup.

Now that you know how to apply your basic eye makeup, touch it up, and remove it, you're on the way to making your eyes speak a more beautiful language. So keep at it—beautiful eyes take practice. Polish and perfect the techniques until you become fluent at this important art!

6/ Color

It's not what you've got, it's what you do with it.
— ANONYMOUS

I DON'T KNOW WHO originally coined this expression, but my mother tells me I repeated it so often while I was growing up she insists on attributing the authorship to me. To this day, my philosophy is: Whatever you've got, color can make it better.

Color is life's great communicator. It's also the spice of my life. Unhampered by words, color crosses the common barriers of language and accent and goes directly to the heart.

Color expresses personality—our aspirations, inclinations, fantasies, even fears.

Color shapes environment. How bland and boring a black-and-white world would be. But just add a splash of color and everything takes on dimension, depth, shadow, and interest.

Color commands attention. It strikes our senses with such intensity that to ignore it would be tantamount to sleeping through a Sir Laurence Olivier performance of Shakespeare. The mere mention of the great actor reminds me of the time many years ago when I was an aspiring young actress and Sir Laurence, or "Mr. Olivier" as he was then called, asked to see me to consider my theatrical talents. My agent, Mrs. Foster, arranged for me to go to his office on South Audley Street, London, for an interview. My big moment came and went. I found out later that he liked my eyes (which, by the way, I felt was the reason I got the chance to meet with him in the first place), but, alas, he didn't like my voice. I was rejected and dejected but I got over it. You can't have everything!

Color uplifts and elevates the essence of everything—especially fashion. There isn't a successful designer around who doesn't count on color to sell silhouette, fit, and fabric.

Color is you. And color psychology, according to the experts, will tell a lot about who you really are. Extroverts, prefer warm, intense colors like reds and yellows, while introverts traditionally lean to the cooler, calmer shades, especially earth tones and neutrals. Color games peg personality types: politicians, performers, even athletes tend toward red (they like the limelight); most salesmen score high on orange; actors favor yellow; teachers lean toward green; writers and philosophers are partial to blue; and designers and musicians love purple.

If the power of color itself isn't enough to make you realize the tremendously important role it plays in our lives, nothing will—and you might just as well resign yourself to having a color IQ equivalent to "battleship gray." But to all those women who treat color as a beauty partner, either daringly or conservatively, I say experiment away the Mono way. That means, have a plan.

Pyramid Color Plan

I have always loved unusual eye makeup colors. If I see a very attractive woman with beautifully made up eyes, and she is using a color that I have not seen before, I ask her what it is. For instance, I have a striking black woman working for me in New York City and one day I noticed she was wearing the most incredible iridescent blue under and around her eyes. Of course, I tried it on myself the next day. I never stop in my search to be innovative and up-to-date, regardless of the fact that I'm in my mid-forties. And I hope I never do. I invent makeup colors the way I imagine an artist experiments with watercolors. The possible combinations are endless and the shades and nuances created can be breathtaking. My approach to eye makeup color isn't complicated—but it is *courageous*. I have always believed that if you're going to get better at anything you have to be willing to take risks. Improving your color IQ is not any different. After all, if you do make a mistake or don't like a particular result, it's the easiest thing in the world to clean your eyes and start again. Once you get the knack of it, you'll wonder how you could have been so "color blind" before.

My Pyramid Color Plan, and I call it that because it's comprised of three very important points, has been the successful basis for thousands of color schemes. So before you experiment with color for your eyes, read and understand these basics that will make color really work for you.

1. COORDINATE COLOR   The proper way to select eye makeup color is *not* by matching it to the color of your eyes. That's an old-fashioned adage with far too many limitations and not enough liberations. For example, if you are blue-eyed, does that mean you can only wear blue eye shadow? Absolutely not! Eye makeup color should be *coordinated* to three aspects:

- your eye color
- your complexion
- your clothes

All these factors should be taken into consideration if you expect to create a successful eye color formula.

2. CONTRAST COLOR   You can wear any makeup color on your eyes just as long as it *contrasts* with your natural eye color and with what you are wearing. For example, if you are determined to wear green eye shadow with your green eyes and green dress, it is best to use a shadow three shades darker, never lighter, than the green of your eyes. Why? Because if you wear a green outfit and your accessories blend in or are even the same color value, you create a monochromatic color scheme with no visible point of attention, and therefore, no focus. You defeat the express purpose of wearing eye makeup—which is to command attention.

Instead, you'll create a much better effect if you contrast colors by wearing green shadow used in conjunction with earth colors, like dusky browns or bronzes. This combination plays color against color—and will do more to play up your beautiful green eyes than green alone. Another possibility for contrast is to eliminate green shadow all together and instead use colors such as pale apricots and deep corals, which are good *compliments* to both the green in your eyes and in your wardrobe.

3. COMBINE COLOR   The success of all eye makeup beauty relies on *combining* colors, not isolating them. Using a single eye makeup color will not give you the subtlety and depth you want to achieve and your eyes deserve. To get the required depth, in general you need to use a *minimum of three shades* which should be applied as follows:

- the lightest shade on the inside corner of the lid
- a medium shade on the center of the lid
- the darkest color on the outer portion of the lid

This technique works extremely well for most women. The sole exception is if you are using corrective makeup to camouflage flaws (see Chapter 4).

Now that the basics of the eye makeup color plan—*coordinating, contrasting,* and *combining*—are in place, let's see how they can relate to the colors of your eyes, your complexion, and your clothes to create beautiful eye makeup color schemes.

Eye Color

Always consider how your *natural* eye color relates to your eye *makeup* color. The color of your eyes will not necessarily determine what color eye makeup you should wear, but it will have some bearing on it. There is only one rule to remember: If you use an eye shadow color that's in the same family as your own eye color, be sure it is *deeper* than your natural eye color—for contrast. Otherwise, it will blend in, fade away, and have no focus. Now let's run down the list of eye colors.

BROWN EYES

Women with brown eyes are the luckiest of all when it comes to color because brown eyes can carry off *any* eye makeup color and look seductively beautiful.

Having brown eyes means you can use colors that range from *the brightest pinks to the darkest browns*. Which colors and how much of them you use will depend on your skin tone, and, of course, your personality. But you are never limited by how dark or light or dramatic a shade may be, as long as you line your eyes properly with kajal to make the whites of the eyes white—so the brown stands out.

BEST MAKEUP BETS FOR BROWN EYES

Shadows	*Kohl*	*Kajal*	*Mascara*
Inner lid: Beige *Center lid:* Rust *Outer lid:* Dark brown	Deep copper	Dark brown or Black	Dark brown or Black
Inner lid: Pink *Center lid:* Deep mauve *Outer lid:* Dark purple	Purple or Wine	Navy or Black	Navy or Black
Inner lid: Pale coral *Center lid:* Copper *Outer lid:* Deep forest green	Dark brown	Hunter green	Black
Inner lid: Gold *Center lid:* Bright coral *Outer lid:* Black	Chocolate brown	Black	Black

BLUE EYES

Even though I love my brown eyes, every now and then I wish I had blue eyes, simply because they look so heavenly (especially Paul Newman's—but I'm not creating makeup for men . . . yet!). Blue eyes look sensational in *all shades of blue*, from the palest sky blue to the deepest royal blue. And blue shadows today are spectacular, especially when compared to years ago when a blue-eyed beauty was lucky if she could find blue shadows in more than light, medium, and dark blue.

But if you have blue eyes, don't restrict yourself to wearing just blues. Blue-eyed women can look smashing in a host of other colors: *mauves, corals, golds, golden bronzes, coppers, grays.* What blue eyes should *avoid* are pale shades of green. Instead of playing up the blue, green tones tend to compete with it, and the result is that neither your eyes nor your eye makeup will carry their own.

BEST MAKEUP BETS FOR BLUE EYES

Shadows	*Kohl*	*Kajal*	*Mascara*
Inner lid: Soft pink *Center lid:* Soft blue *Outer lid:* Deep smoky blue	Gray or Navy	Navy or Black	Navy or Black
Inner lid: White *Center lid:* Silver gray *Outer lid:* Charcoal gray	Soft gray or Black	Navy or Black	Navy or Black
Inner lid: Pale pink *Center lid:* Mauve *Outer lid:* Deep purple	Black	Plum	Plum
Inner lid: White *Center lid:* Lime green *Outer lid:* Mauve	Wine	Plum	Plum

HAZEL EYES

These fascinating, changeable eyes can swing from blue to blue-gray to green, green-yellow, and even green-brown. They look best when made up in *neutral* shades, such as *gray, smoky blue, green,* or *taupe.* Neutral shadows allow the hazel eyes to change to whatever the influencing color may be—clothing, environment, etc.

For hazel blue eyes: any shade of *smoky blue, mauve, pink,* or *purple* will give a radiant glow to the blue.

For hazel gray eyes: try using *charcoal grays, silvers,* and *pale aquamarine.*

For hazel green, yellow-green, or *green-brown eyes:* colors such as *copper, gold,* and *peach* are best.

BEST MAKEUP BETS FOR HAZEL EYES

Shadows	Kohl	Kajal	Mascara
Inner lid: Bone *Center lid:* Medium beige *Outer lid:* Deep taupe	Taupe	Dark brown or Black	Dark brown or Black
Inner lid: Light jade *Center lid:* Emerald *Outer lid:* Deep forest green	Forest green	Dark brown or Black	Dark brown or Black
Inner lid: Pale pink *Center lid:* Pale mauve *Outer lid:* Deep mauve	Purple	Black	Black
Inner lid: Pale coral *Center lid:* Golden copper *Outer lid:* Deep rust	Copper	Black	Black

VIOLET EYES

Violet eyes are truly exceptional. If you are blessed with them you can wear shadows of *greens, golds, ambers, blues, purples,* and *mauves.* These are all contrasting colors that will further emphasize the unique beauty of the violet.

BEST MAKEUP BETS FOR VIOLET EYES

Shadows	*Kohl*	*Kajal*	*Mascara*
Inner lid: Soft pink *Center lid:* Medium blue *Outer lid:* Deep charcoal	Black	Black	Black
Inner lid: Light violet *Center lid:* Mauve *Outer lid:* Deep purple	Purple	Black	Black
Inner lid: Beige *Center lid:* Light brown *Outer lid:* Dark brown	Dark brown	Black	Black
Inner lid: White *Center lid:* Pale pink *Outer lid:* Navy	Black	Plum	Plum

GREEN EYES

Pure green eyes are so spectacular they can cause strangers to stare. And why not? Though green eyes are usually coupled with fair skin, sometimes, when they're set against the darker backdrop of an olive or tawny complexion, the effect is like fireworks. I like to see green eyes made up with shadow combinations of *medium green, yellow-beige,* and *deep bronze.* If you like a more natural effect, stick with bronze and brown shades.

BEST MAKEUP BETS FOR GREEN EYES

Shadows	*Kohl*	*Kajal*	*Mascara*
Inner lid: White gold *Center lid:* Bronze *Outer lid:* Dark brown/ rust	Soft brown	Dark brown or Black	Dark brown or Black
Inner lid: Yellow gold *Center lid:* Apricot *Outer lid:* Deep coral/ rust	Copper brown or Rust brown	Dark brown or Black	Dark brown or Black
Inner lid: White *Center lid:* Bronze *Outer lid:* Olive	Chocolate brown	Hunter green	Black
Inner lid: Gold *Center lid:* Beige *Outer lid:* Deep olive	Forest green	Black	Black

BLACK-BROWN EYES

This is indeed a most striking eye color even without any eye make-up. Women with exceptionally dark black-brown eyes can go wild with color. If you are one of these fortunate women I suggest you wear eye makeup in *gold, red,* and *green* shades. The more vibrant the better. You will look stunning.

BEST MAKEUP BETS FOR BLACK-BROWN EYES

Shadows	*Kohl*	*Kajal*	*Mascara*
Inner lid: Pink *Center lid:* Cerise *Outer lid:* Deep wine	Wine	Black	Black
Inner lid: Gold *Center lid:* Rust *Outer lid:* Deep brown	Rust or Copper	Black or Dark brown	Black or Dark brown
Inner lid: White *Center lid:* Gray *Outer lid:* Charcoal gray	Silver or Gray	Black	Black
Inner lid: Pale blue *Center lid:* Light pink *Outer lid:* Navy blue	Navy	Navy	Black

Complexion

No matter what your skin tone may be, you are not restricted to one set of eye makeup colors. Nor are there any rigid rules to follow. As long as color is applied properly, a woman today has the advantage of an unlimited selection at her fingertips. However, you will look twice as stunning if you coordinate your skin tone with certain eye makeup colors and avoid others. The following guidelines are intended to help you make the most of what you've got.

FAIR COMPLEXION

Select *brown, cream,* or *peach* shades of eye shadow, as these will help give extra depth to your eyes. If you are looking for that little extra attention, apply a *yellow-gold, white-gold,* or *pale coral highlighter* color. Dot on highlighter color in either of two ways: (1) on the center of your brow bone, blending it right up to your eyebrow or (2) on the center of your lid, blending across. These golden and iridescent shades make other colors seem dull by comparison, and once you become comfortable using them, you'll get hooked on their shine.

Dark brown, black, blue, or *gray* liners work best for fair complexions. If you contour with pencil, use neutral colors like *soft gray* or *light brown.* If you prefer a more iridescent finish, use neutral iridescents such as *mauve, dark navy blue,* or even *dark brown.* Your color possibilities are extremely broad since most shades show up well against fair skin. And they'll also add extra dimension to the shape of your eye.

FRECKLED COMPLEXION

Women with freckles should come out of the closet and use their special pigmentation to make a statement. I say work with your freckles and stop camouflaging them! If you have a freckled complexion you can achieve a fabulous effect by using eye shadows and highlighters in colors such as *coral, deep royal blue,* and *midnight blue. Brown* shades can also look stunning on your eyes as long as they are true brown and not gray-brown, as this combination will tend to make your eyes look muddy. A *coppery brown* or even a *seashell peach* are also very flattering. Women with freckled skin should *avoid* mauves and pink tones since these colors can make the eyes look sore and bruised.

OLIVE COMPLEXION

The most flattering eye colors to use for olive-toned skin are any and all shades of *pinks, blues, mauves,* and *coppery browns*. These shades counteract the natural sallowness of the skin and tend to add a pink glow to the yellow cast. Women with olive complexions should *avoid* using green or yellow eye shadows as they will only draw attention to the sallowness of your skin.

RUDDY COMPLEXION

This complexion calls for especially careful color selection. Any eye shadow color with too much pink, red, or purple will play up the uneven redness of the skin. The shadow colors to accentuate are *taupes, true blues, browns,* and *bronzes,* as they have no red in them and will help balance out your skin tone. *Soft gray* or *silver-gray* can also work extremely well. Avoid darker grays, however, as they will only darken and muddy the look instead of uplifting and lightening it.

TAWNY COMPLEXION

Tawny-colored skin is skin that is brownish-yellow. This type of complexion creates a natural shadow around the eye area which, in turn, tends to give the eye a sunken look. To counteract this effect, use shadows in *bright corals, ambers, coppers,* and *bronzes,* as they will brighten up the eye and bring it out. Similarly, women with tawny complexions should *avoid* shadow colors such as rose, peach, and fuschia as they give the impression that your eyes are smaller and receded further than they actually are.

BLACK COMPLEXION

Black skin is the most complicated of all to choose eye makeup colors for. On the one hand, it can carry high-intensity color like no other skin tone. On the other hand, black skin also absorbs color more readily than other skin tones and a regular application of color will not even show up. You need to choose eye shadow color for black skin tones thoughtfully and carefully. The shades you choose can and should be a lot stronger, more vivid, and vibrant in order to create good contrast. Avoid all pastel colors, as they'll look "painted on" and fake. Also eliminate deep, dull colors from your shadow spectrum because they just blend into the skin and have a tendency to make the black complexion appear ruddy and even grayish.

The best eye shadow colors for black skin are *bright greens, brilliant corals, lively purples,* and *vibrant wine reds.* These shades have enough intensity to hold up and really highlight the eye. An *iridescent pencil,* especially in mauve, works wonders under the bottom lashes. A touch of *gold highlighter* on the lid will lighten up the dark eye. A *black-brown shadow* to shade in the crease will help to dramatically define the eye shape.

"SUMMER" COMPLEXION

Proper coloring of the "summer eye," when your natural complexion is hidden beneath a beautiful tan, is something most women don't pay enough attention to. Whether you realize it or not, every natural skin tone tans during the summer. Of course, the degree of tan can vary from a barely perceptible highlight to a deep, dark glow. All the eye colors you normally wear will look completely different against suntanned skin. So be sure you coordinate your summer eye color palette with your summer complexion. In general, the colors you choose should be a bit more vivid and glimmery. For example, *golden eye shadows mixed with coppery or coral tones* really complement a tanned complexion. Lining the inside rim of the eyes with *black kajal* is a must and will set off these colors beautifully. If you like to use liner, also try lining just underneath your lower lashes with a *bright* or *pastel-colored iridescent.*

When I have a tan, I love to be innovative with eye color. I'm sure this statement will horrify some of you who can't believe a woman in the cosmetic business sits in the sun—but I do. Why? Because I believe that moderate sunning with lots of protective cream is not harmful, and, besides, it makes *me* feel good! Summer is the time when I am totally relaxed and can play and experiment with creating new eye makeup looks. Last summer, for example, I used an electric red, not only to accent the tan on my cheeks but as an eye shadow as well. To this I added a little gold and the effect was stunning. Every woman can support more eye makeup color during the summer months when she's tanned than she can during the winter when the light is cold and her complexion is paler. So why not take advantage of the color freedom and have a spree with "hot" eye colors? You'll have some fun. I guarantee you that. And you'll probably be surprised at how good you'll feel and look.

Fashion Color

The colors of what you are wearing play a major role in determining what the overall color formula of your eye makeup should be. Try to coordinate either the main fashion color of your wardrobe or an accent color to your eye makeup palette. Naturally, if you are wearing a red blouse you wouldn't wear red eye shadow—but you could use a beautiful shade of coral. Remember, you don't want to *match* color. What you're after is *coordination* and *contrast*. I often accent my eyes under the lower lashes with an iridescent pencil in a shade that complements my dress—in the same way women wear jewelry to complement an outfit. For instance, if I were wearing a turquoise dress I might use a deep peacock eye shadow to bring the whole color tapestry together.

In order to help you get on the correct color track, the handy "Colorscope" in the color insert of this book lists some of the most popular fashion colors and keys them to the eye makeup colors that are most appropriate. The fashion colors are divided into three categories:

CLASSICS: *navy, gray, black, burgundy*
NEUTRALS: *beige, light blue, off white, lavender*
ACCENTS: trend colors like *red, yellow, hot pink, bright blue*

Even if you have lots of other colors in your wardrobe, this palette will provide you with a solid foundation from which you can build outward. So experiment away, and have fun.

Whether you're twenty-five or sixty-five, color is the "be all and end all" of beauty and what making up your eyes and face is really all about. Color is the spice of a woman's life. And once you learn how to use it, you'll find it allows you to express yourself like nothing else will. I can't encourage you enough to turn on to color. Don't be afraid. Don't be timid. Beautiful colors will actually make you *feel* happy, so why deny yourself the fun of seeing how much more attractive you really can look? You'll fall in love with the new, "colorful" you—and so will others.

7/ Night Eyes

She walks in beauty, like the night
Of cloudless climes and starry skies;
And all that's best of dark and bright
Meet in her aspect and her eyes.
— LORD BYRON

NIGHTTIME IS THE TIME a woman can go all out for drama and glamour in her eye makeup—and get away with it. I love the liberation and freedom of evening makeup when you can cut loose from the basics and experiment with stunning eye colors—like fuchsia, coral, and purple—and carry them off with style.

Every woman should think of her face, especially her eyes and the area surrounding them, as an artist's canvas and should use her eye makeup to approach them that way—as the surface on which a work of art is about to be created. There are, of course, many different styles of art; so it is with eye makeup. Keep in mind that your eye makeup for the evening should, in general, be quite different from your daytime look. What works for the office, home, or executive life may be too subdued to properly illuminate the eye for evening. *Night eyes should be made up more strikingly and dramatically than daytime eyes,* especially since interior evening lighting tends to reduce contrast and color intensity. So the more eye color you apply (skillfully, of course), the more alluring your eyes will look.

Now let's find out how to create the basic night eye.

The Basic Night Eye

Getting ready for a special event or special occasion can be one of the most pleasurable—even sensuous—times in a woman's life. Unfortunately, setting aside a block of time to make this magic transformation is not always possible. I know and can speak from experience on this as, like so many other women, I always seem to be doing things on the run. But somehow we manage. What it really boils down to is planning ahead. Simple as it seems, reserving the time you need so that you're not rushed will make "evening-izing" your life a lot easier.

I have found that the best way to get ready for the night ahead is to take ten or fifteen minutes to simply relax. Lie on your bed with your eyes closed and place one of the homemade "tired-eye tonics" on them (see pages 108–11).

As you gradually unwind, decide what you're going to wear and then mentally tick off what *style* eye makeup will coordinate best with your outfit. With this in mind, select two or three eye shadow colors that will best emphasize the *color palette* of your outfit. Rest a minute more. Now you're ready to start with the basic nighttime makeup. Here's my system:

1. Cleanse your face well and apply your usual moisturizer.

2. Now, pat a thin layer of concealing cream above and below the eye to make sure your skin tone is perfectly even and balanced before you start to apply any color. Concealing cream (or eye shadow base, as it is sometimes referred to) brightens up the eye area and also creates a good "grabbing" surface on which you'll be able to apply smooth, thin layers of color. When color is applied this way it won't crease or wear off as fast and you won't have to fuss with touching up your eye makeup half way through the evening.

3. Using a small blusher brush, take a bit of white-gold iridescent powder and make a V shape starting at the outside corner of the eye over the temple and down the top of the cheekbone. Apply a little more white-gold powder, dotting it down the center of the lid directly over the pupil of the eyes. This will catch the light and call attention to the eye.

4. Next, gently apply black kajal to the inside rims of your eyes, both upper and lower, to create instant drama.

5. Apply at least three thin coats of your regular mascara, waiting for each coat to dry before applying the next. You can *never* apply too much mascara in the evening, provided, of course, that you do it evenly, layer upon layer.

6. Apply a bright blue mascara to the tips of the lashes to achieve a lush, extra-long lash.

7. Use an iridescent pencil to line the eye area directly under the lower lash line. This will give you that vibrant color you need at night.

INSTANT DAY-INTO-NIGHT SWITCH

Even if your busy schedule sends you straight from the office to a party or the theater and you don't have time to redo your eye makeup from scratch before going out, don't worry. With just a few simple steps you can transform your basic daytime eye into an alluring night eye. Here's how:

• First, touch up under the eye area with a concealing cream one shade lighter than your skin tone. This brightens the eye, hides those end-of-day shadows and circles, and helps your eyes appear larger.

• Next, apply either black or dark blue pencil just under the lower lash line. Blend this with a fine-point brush, sweeping it up from the corners to create an "uplifted" look. Blend the pencil into the eye shadow you already have on and the outer corners of your eyes will instantly take on added emphasis.

• Highlight with an iridescent powder or pencil just under the brow and down the center of the lid.

• Add one or two more thin coats of mascara.

• Lightly dust just a touch of iridescent powder high on your cheekbone to illuminate your eyes even more. Iridescent powder should be applied very subtly, just above your blusher; be sure to blend it well so there are no harsh lines. The finished effect is extremely flattering to any woman's face because it brings your eyes and cheekbones into prominence as you turn your face toward the light. One of my favorites is a mixture of loose pink powder and gold powder. It is so stunning on the cheekbone that eyes are automatically drawn to the face that's wearing it. Try it and experience the reaction for yourself.

Five Beautiful Eye Makeup Looks for Evening

Now you're ready to try some elegant, high-fashion evening eye makeup looks. With just a little practice you can become accomplished in achieving each effect. The key is to remember that successful eye makeup depends upon the even blending of tones and colors. So be sure you brush on the different colors smoothly to create one continuous flow—like a rainbow. If the colors are so rigidly demarcated that they look like separate bands of color, you'll ruin the effect and wind up with eyes that look smaller rather than larger.

Here are five truly beautiful looks you'll have a lot of fun duplicating.

THE GILDED EYE

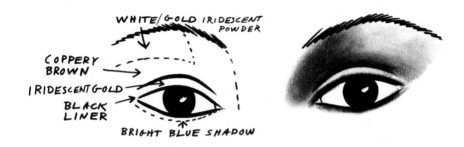

The "gilded eye" is like the pot of gold at the end of the rainbow. It is a rich, elegant, yet subtle look. Here's how to achieve it:

1. Pat on a thin layer of *concealing cream* all around the eye area.
2. Brush on a thin coat of *white-gold loose powder* all over the eye area from the lid to the brow. This acts as a highlighter base color.
3. Brush an *iridescent gold eye shadow* on your eyelid.
4. Follow with a *coppery brown shadow*. Starting at the inside corner of your eye, blend the shadow into the crease only and extend it out to the edge of your brow. This will create a soft, shapely effect.
5. With a very fine eye liner brush, apply *black liner* in short strokes as close to the base of the upper lashes as possible, working from the inside corner of the eye to where the lashes end. This will give the illusion of much thicker, more lustrous lashes.

6. With *black kajal,* rim the inside of the upper and lower lids.

7. Brush *bright blue shadow* on the area just under the lower lashes to make the whole eye come alive. (A more subdued blue will look wishy-washy.)

8. Layer on three thin coats of *black mascara,* letting each coat dry thoroughly before applying the next.

9. Finish off lashes by touching the tips of them with *bright blue mascara.*

10. Complete the glamour by dusting on a *white-gold iridescent powder* in a V shape, with the broad part of the V under the brow and the narrow point of the V tapering down to the center of the lid.

THE BUTTERFLY EYE

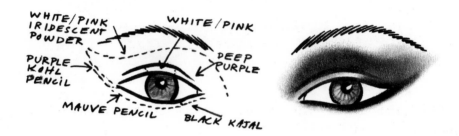

There's nothing more graceful than a butterfly gliding through the air, spreading its wings to reflect its unique color. This was the inspiration for the beautiful "butterfly eye."

1. Gently pat on *concealing cream* all around the eye.

2. Apply a *white-pink iridescent powder* to the center of the lid and the brow bone. This will bring your brow bone out and draw attention to the center of the eye.

3. Next, apply a *deep purple shadow.* Start at the inside corner of the eye and blend it in along the crease only, stopping at the outside corner of the lid.

4. On the outside corner of your eye, apply *purple kohl pencil* in a V shape and blend in toward your nose, stopping at the center of the lid. This will add extra depth.

5. Gently rim the inside of your lids with *black kajal*. This will set off the bright shadow colors so that your natural eye color is still the center of attention.

6. With *mauve pencil,* rim just under the lower lash line.

7. Complete the look by applying no less than three coats of *black mascara.*

THE RADIANT RAINBOW EYE

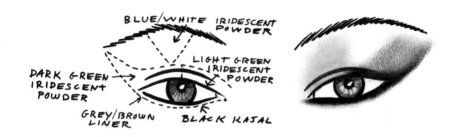

The "rainbow eye" is an unusual and glamorous look created to enhance the natural beauty of every eye color.

1. Pat on *concealing cream* on the lower lid and above the eye from lid to brow.

2. Lightly dust the entire lid area with *translucent powder.*

3. Brush on a *light green iridescent powder* all over the lid, slightly blending the powder into the crease of your eye.

4. On the outer edge of the eye, extend a *dark green iridescent powder* in an "up" sweep. Work toward the brow and blend into the crease.

5. Highlight the center of the lid and under the brow bone with a small amount of *blue-white iridescent powder.*

6. Rim the inner lids with *black kajal.*

7. Line the area directly under the lower lashes with a *gray-brown eye shadow.*

8. Layer on three coats of *black mascara.*

9. Finish by tipping lashes with *bright blue mascara.*

THE EASTERN EYE

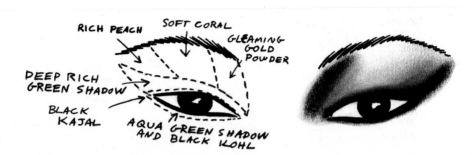

The mysterious "Eastern eye" is like no other and this exotic eye shape, deep-set and dark, is fascinating to re-create with makeup.

1. Gently pat on *concealing cream* below the eye and on the lid right up to the brow.

2. Dust this area lightly with a *translucent powder*.

3. Darken the entire lid area upward and out with a *rich, deep green shadow*.

4. Brush on a little *silvery black powder* close to the lash area on top of the lid.

5. Starting at the inside corner of the lid, subtly blend in the following colors outward to contour the eye: Begin with *gleaming gold powder*, then add a *soft coral*, then a *rich peach*, and finally a *pastel green*. Overlap one color into the next in an arch from above the already-darkened lid up to the brow.

6. Darken under the lower lashes with an *aqua-green shadow* and *black kohl*.

7. Rim the insides of upper and lower lids with *black kajal*.

8. Finish with three coats of *black mascara*.

THE SULTRY EYE

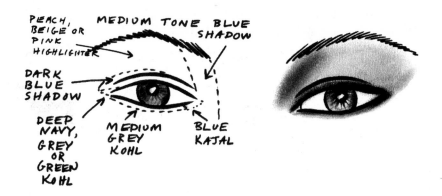

PEACH, BEIGE OR PINK HIGHLIGHTER

MEDIUM TONE BLUE SHADOW

DARK BLUE SHADOW

DEEP NAVY, GREY OR GREEN KOHL

MEDIUM GREY KOHL

BLUE KAJAL

The dark, smoky allure of this eye is a look every woman can wear. The "sultry eye," in my opinion, is the sexiest eye makeup look a woman can have. Be sure you're ready for the consequences!

1. Gently pat on *concealing cream* over the entire eye area.

2. Blend in *peach, beige,* or *pink highlighter* over the eye area, covering the lid right up to the brow.

3. Starting at the outside corner of the eyelid and concentrating the color there, blend in a *medium-tone blue shadow,* either matte or iridescent. Work the blue into the crease and up toward the bridge of the nose and then up to the brow.

4. At the outer corner of the lid, brush a *darker shade of blue shadow* right on top of the medium blue, blending in the color until it fades away into the center of the lid. This will add extra depth to the eye.

5. Line the base of the upper lashes with *deep gray, navy,* or *black kohl.*

6. Line the inside rims, both upper and lower, with *dark blue kajal.* The blue will reflect on the white of the eye to make your natural eye color appear truer and more dramatic.

7. Use a brush to blend in *medium gray kohl* just under the lower lashes, leaving just a smoky haze of color.

8. Apply a tiny bit of *vaseline* to your brow brush and brush brows upward. This will keep them in place and add a hint of shine.

9. Layer on three thin coats of *black mascara.*

What's important to remember, day or night, is that makeup is very personal and also very much a reflection of your personality. Every woman is unique, so learn the basics and then use them in a way that makes you feel comfortable. After all, it's *your* face the world sees, not someone else's. And only when you *feel* beautiful will others see you that way.

NIGHT EYES—Step-by-Step

...cealing cream hides shadows and brightens ...ye.

Highlighter catches light and opens up the eye.

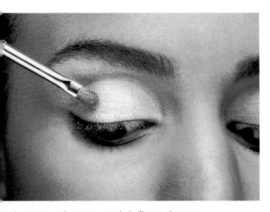

...r dresses, shapes, and defines the eye.

Kajal brings out eye color and whitens eye whites.

...l creates a thicker lower lash line and balances ...makeup.

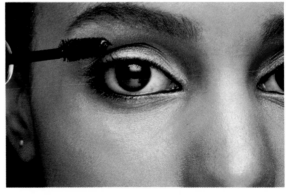

Mascara adds drama and completes the eye.

5-MINUTE MISTAKE-PROOF
DAYTIME EYE MAKEUP
—Step-by-Step

Brush brow into natural arch.

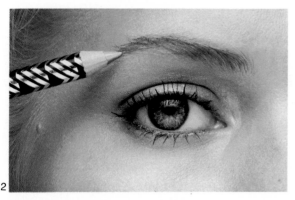

Pencil in brow with feathery strokes.

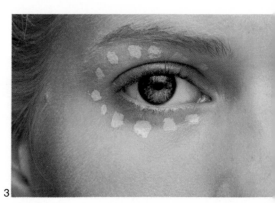

Apply concealing cream to cover circles and shadows.

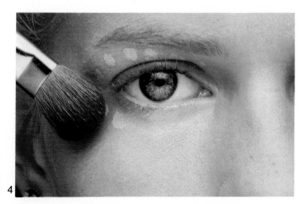

Blend in.

Powder eyelid—it acts as a base for shadow colors.

ntour and shape with color in the classic V.

Highlighter applied to brow bone area draws attention to eye.

er, above and below, balances and shapes the e.

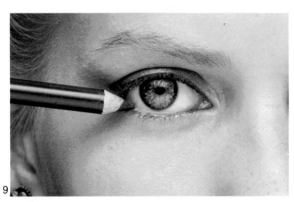

Rim inside lids with kajal for whiter eye whites and instant drama.

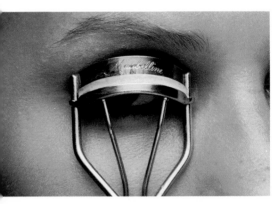

rl lashes—a must for giving an up-sweep to the shes.

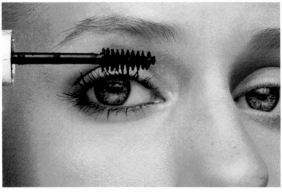

Apply mascara, at least two coats, to complete the daytime eye.

COLORSCOPE

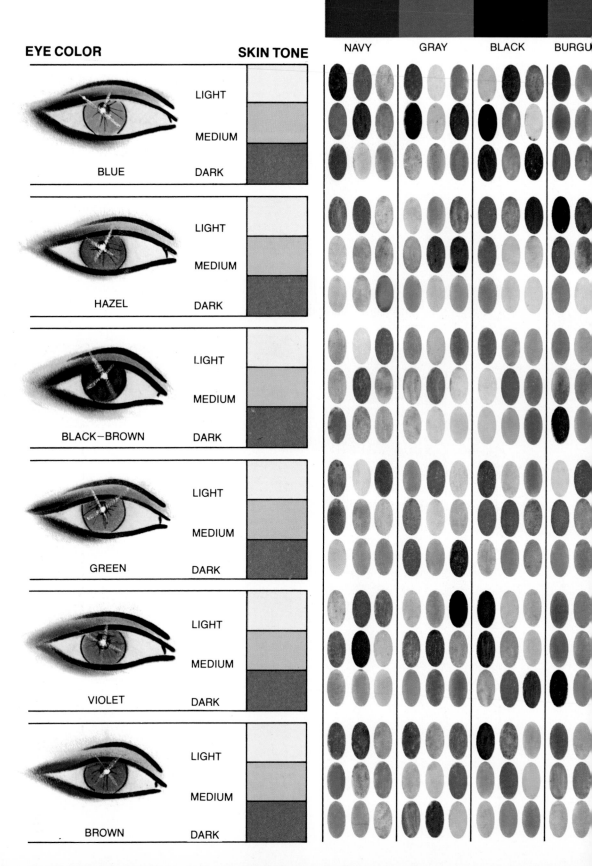

CLASSICS

EYE COLOR **SKIN TONE** NAVY GRAY BLACK BURGU

BLUE — LIGHT / MEDIUM / DARK

HAZEL — LIGHT / MEDIUM / DARK

BLACK—BROWN — LIGHT / MEDIUM / DARK

GREEN — LIGHT / MEDIUM / DARK

VIOLET — LIGHT / MEDIUM / DARK

BROWN — LIGHT / MEDIUM / DARK

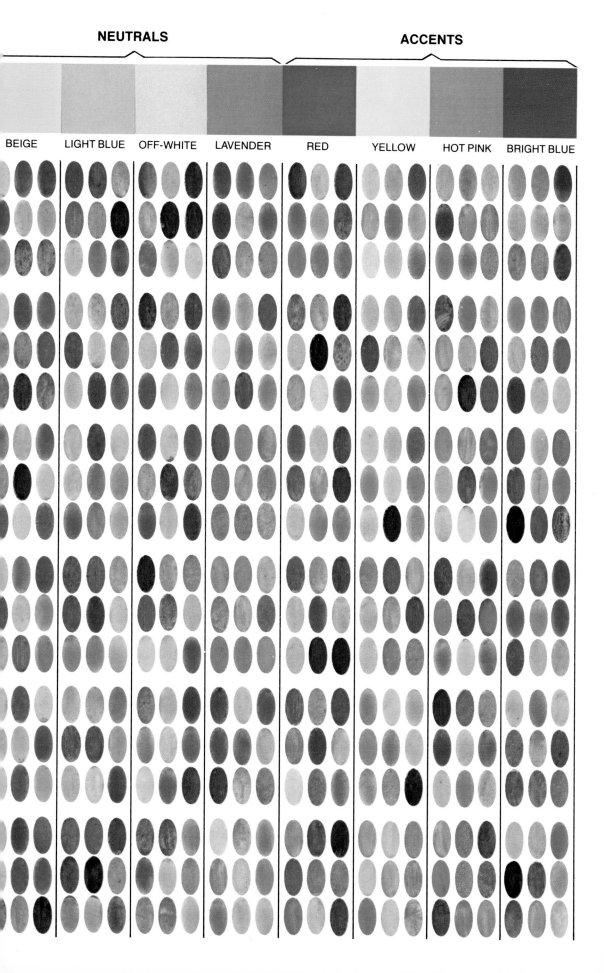

NEUTRALS   ACCENTS

BEIGE   LIGHT BLUE   OFF-WHITE   LAVENDER   RED   YELLOW   HOT PINK   BRIGHT BLUE

BEAUTIFUL EYE MAKEUP LOOKS
FOR EVENING

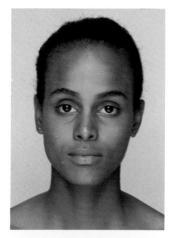  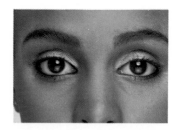

THE GILDED EYE: Eyes are rich with golden gleam, glitter, and elegance.

THE BUTTERFLY EYE: Eyes take wing in brilliant, bright colors.

THE RADIANT RAINBOW EYE: An unusual, glamorous look that enhances every color eye.

THE EASTERN EYE: Mysteriously muted colors create an extraordinary exotic eye.

THE SULTRY EYE: A sexy, smoky, alluring night eye.

YOUTHFUL EYES AT ANY AGE

THE OVER-30 EYE: Focus highlighter on brow area for an instant uplift. Don't forget concealing cream for that extra shadowing under the eyes.

THE OVER-40 EYE: Be glamorous. Don't avoid color. Use matte shadows and concentrate on shaping the eye with kajal and liner.

THE OVER-60 EYE: The skilled use of color can do wonders for any woman. Take special care to blend and smooth in eye colors, especially over an older, crepy lid.

8 / Special Effect Theatrics / Special Occasion Eyes

But love, first learned in a lady's eyes,
Lives not alone immured in the brain.
— WILLIAM SHAKESPEARE,
Love's Labour's Lost

Special Effect Theatrics

GLITTER

When you really want to pull out the stops on glamour, glitter will help you light up the room. I love the fantasy of glitter. In fact, I have sometimes been referred to as the original "glitter queen."

Glitter is a very feminine, yet provocative way of adorning your face. Glitter, tiny metallic particles radiating gem fire, is available in a variety of colors, including diamond and gold. (If you can't get the real things, this is as near as I can come to it for you!)

To use: Simply stroke a very tiny bit onto the skin. The invisible gel in which the particles are mixed holds the glitter in place. Glitter will wash off during your regular cleansing routine.

A note to skeptics: Glitter as a beauty aid *is* unusual, and for this reason many women are reluctant to use it. If you are one of these women, all I can say to you is that you never know until you try! Deciding how much and where you want to use glitter is an individual matter. Glitter can be applied so discreetly that only *you* will know you have it on. Even so, I guarantee that when you wear glitter you will *feel* more alluring and more daring than you ever have before.

FOR A BALLROOM FLOOR If you will be gliding across a ballroom floor romantically lit by dimmed chandeliers and the dress you're planning to wear has thin straps, and a plunging neckline: Smooth a thin film of glitter across your shoulders and around your back, letting just a touch spill into the cleavage. If you want a more conservative look, simply create a delicate neckline with glitter by lightly encircling your throat with it. Whichever way you choose, finish by adding a very subtle touch of glitter to your cheekbones, being careful to keep the particles away from your eyes.

FOR A DINNER PARTY If you're going to a dinner party where you'll be seated most of the evening and the lights will be fairly bright: Work a small amount of glitter through your hair with your fingers or a comb, or create highlighting streaks in your hair by adding glitter here and there. You might want to try concentrating a bit of glitter on your arms and hands, so that lifting a wine glass to your lips or passing the salt becomes a gleaming gesture. How much glitter you use depends entirely upon how dramatic you want to look. Glitter strategy is entirely up to you.

FOR A NIGHTCLUB If you're going to a nightclub where the room will be darkened: Try shifting glitter kilowattage to the lower parts of the body. Applying a touch of glitter to your shoes, stockings (especially if they're a black shade), skirt, or pants will give you a subtly sexy allure every time you move.

"LES MOUCHES"

FOR THE MOUCHE

The sun and moon by her bright eyes
Eclipsed and darkened in the skies
Are but black patches that she wears
Cut into sun and moons and stars.
— SAMUEL BUTLER,
Hudibras

When the mood strikes, wearing a beauty mark can be the height of womanly appeal. Some famous actresses, like Elizabeth Taylor, make a point of playing up a well-placed mole, that is, a mole located in a place on the face that signifies beauty such as near the eyes or above the mouth. These mystery marks are extremely provocative if they're done

correctly. But a word of caution: You absolutely *must* be the type that can carry this effect off; otherwise, you'll end up looking like the wicked witch. Still, if you have the dramatic personality to pull it off, naughty can definitely be nice. Don't be afraid to try this unusual beauty technique. Chances are that if you've seen other women who have done it successfully and thought you could, too, you probably can!

FOR DRAMATIC EFFECT Place a pretty-colored rhinestone, such as a rose or sapphire, near your eyes or mouth. Simply put a tiny drop of eyelash glue on the back of the stone and carefully stick it onto your skin. You can remove it with a gentle pull.

FOR A SOFTER APPEAL Try the classic "mouche," or black beauty mark. Years ago, these were made of black velvet and were pasted on the face. They can still be purchased in cosmetic boutiques or specialty pharmacies, but the easiest way to apply a mouche is simply to use a very dark black kajal pencil and dot one on. The kajal will wash off when you cleanse your face. The classic mouche shape is round, and it can be worn with panache by even the most conservative women. However, diamond-, club-, spade-, and heart-shaped mouches can also be nice if you're really out to stack the deck and get your man's attention.

Special Occasion Eyes

There are special times in our lives—marriages, graduations, vacations, working, entertaining—special seasons and activities when our normal beauty regimen and makeup look need to adapt to accommodate the situation. No one makeup look will work for every situation, so be flexible and willing to change. Change is the secret of all great and lasting beauties. Only when you stay flexible will you maximize your own best assets. With that in mind, let me share a few tips for special occasion eye makeup.

THE WORKING EYE

Under no circumstances should a smart business woman ever appear totally without eye makeup! However, what business you're in is definitely a factor in how you make up your eyes. For example, a woman in the fashion or beauty business can certainly wear more eye makeup on the job than a woman who works in a corporate environment or is a teacher. Keep in mind that, in general, what you're striving for is a well-integrated, professional look. Accordingly, your daytime eye makeup should be basic, nothing extreme or too colorful. Matte shadows in neutral colors are classic and well-suited to office wear. Equally important, be sure to apply your eye makeup correctly in the morning so you won't have to spend precious time touching up during the busy day.

When applying for a job, remember that first impressions are important, so play down your eye makeup, especially at the initial interview. You don't want it to distract from your personality.

THE SPORTING EYE

If you're an active sportswoman, the general rule of thumb is to try to look as attractive as you can while wearing as little eye makeup as possible. Stick to waterproof mascara since perspiration will cause any other type of mascara to run off. There are also waterproof cream eye shadows which hold up far better than regular shadows during a swim or tennis match. But be careful with these formulations. They have a tendency to dry lashes and skin, so only use them when you must. At other times, use your regular eye makeup.

THE AT-HOME EYE

Too many women fall into the rut of not putting on eye makeup unless they have a reason to go somewhere. I strongly disagree with this kind of thinking. A woman should look her best *all the time,* even if the only eyes that will see her belong to her landlady or the mailman. Looking attractive is important, even if you stay home all day or if the only place you're going is to the grocery store—you never know who will stop by or who you'll run into. Most important, when you wear eye makeup you'll look better and feel better about yourself. Being well-groomed is a way of life for attractive women.

It's not necessary to apply a full eye makeup for at-home wear; a coat of mascara, a quick stroke of eye shadow, and kajal to rim inside the eyelids is plenty and will do wonders for your psyche.

THE GALA EYE

This is the no-limit eye, the dramatic, special eye for that super-special occasion. Start by reading the "Beautiful Eye Makeup Looks for Evening" on pages 75–80. Even if you don't yet have the event to match the eye makeup, experiment with each look. Remember, at night anything goes. And the more color you use, the better—provided, of course, you apply it tastefully and the color suits your personality. For special occasions, use more eye liner and highlighter, too. Be creative!

THE FIRST EYE

It seems little girls are getting older younger. I've found that many girls begin to pay serious attention to their looks and want to beautify their eyes as early as fourteen years of age. The guideline for young girls who are just beginning to experiment with eye makeup should be to start out *simply:* a little bit of liner; a very soft, muted eye shadow color, such as a brown or a smoky gray, lightly brushed onto the lid; one thin coat of mascara. That's it until the next birthday.

THE BRIDAL EYE

In order to keep that white, innocent, bridal look, your makeup for this most special occasion should be understated and elegant. However, keep in mind that there will be lots of picture taking. Though your eye makeup should not be dramatic, you should be wearing enough eye color to guarantee the success of the photographs. Also, remember that a matte shadow will photograph better than an iridescent shadow.

In addition to lots of pictures, there will probably be lots of crying. So, if you're likely to shed a few tears of your own, try using a waterproof mascara, and don't wear any eye makeup that will run too easily. Stay away from eye pencils and stick to eye powders which are more durable.

As for eye shadow color, any color will work with white, but try coordinating your eye colors to the bridal-party colors—matching them as best you can to the flowers, gowns, or tuxedos, especially if they are not white.

9/ Eyeglasses and Contact Lenses

She is not fair to outward view
As many maidens be;
Her loveliness I never knew
Until she smiled on me:
Oh! then I saw her eye was bright,
A well of love, a spring of light
                    HARTLEY COLERIDGE,
                "Song, She is Not Fair"

EYES AND EYEGLASSES can be one of the best beauty partnerships in town—if you know how to choose the frames that are most flattering to your face and features.

Since eyes are my business, women are always asking me questions. And women who wear eyeglasses and lenses are no exception. One of the questions I hear most often is, "What's the best shape glasses for me?"

Well, there was a time when eyeglasses were not fashionable, but thank heaven times have changed. Glasses are not only fashionable, they can be high fashion, and you can now choose from as many shapes and colors as there are designers to create them. Frame shapes aren't pure geometrics any more, either; they come in all kinds of subtle variations of squares, ovals, and rounds. There are even frame styles that mix shapes, such as those that are rounded on top and octagonal on the bottom.

With such a wealthy array to choose from, determining what's best for you requires more care and attention than simply choosing a frame that goes with the shape of your face. Other factors enter the picture as well, such as how you wear your hair (which means if your hairdo changes from daytime to evening, your glasses should change accordingly); what kind of eye makeup you use; the proportion of your eyes (large or small); the positioning of your eyes in relation to your nose (close-set or wide-set); and the activities you're involved in. Every woman who wears glasses can add many more relevant factors. And please do, because the more factors about your face and lifestyle you take into consideration, the better able you'll be to select the eyeglass style that's best for you.

Frames and Face Shapes

Let's talk about frame size and style in conjunction with face shapes first. Remember that the shape of your face alone will not determine what kind of glasses will look best on your face. Whether your frame is large or small, it should be proportionate to your face and your stature (height, girth). Try to stand in front of a full-length mirror when trying on frames. It's the only way to get a true idea of overall proportion.

Frame size can work for you when it's correct or against you when it's not. For example, if you have small, close-set eyes, a large frame that extends beyond the eye to the sides of your face will only accentuate the fact that your eyes are set close to the nose. It's much more flattering for you to wear a smaller frame. If, on the other hand, you have large, wide-set eyes, a frame that's too small will cut off your eyes on the sides, making them seem even farther apart from each other and your nose. Too often women with well-proportioned faces choose frames that create an appearance of disproportion. When a face is not well proportioned, the frame should never emphasize the disproportion; rather it should be fitted to *de-emphasize* it. Of course, when choosing a frame you must remember to take your hair color, hairstyle, and skin tone into consideration, as they may alter the balance slightly.

Now, let's discuss the five classic face shapes and the frames that are best suited to fit their specific proportions:

THE OVAL FACE   Just as the almond-shaped eye is the perfectly shaped eye, so the oval face is the perfectly shaped face. It is ideally proportioned, with the top half identical to the bottom half. Leonardo Da Vinci's "Mona Lisa" is a classic example of this face shape. If you are blessed with it, you can wear just about any kind of frame design. However, if your oval face tends to be on the thin side, opt for frames that are slightly more substantial; they will help fill out and balance your face. Contrariwise, if your beautiful oval face tends to be a bit on the heavy side, select a more delicate frame (wire-framed aviators are an excellent choice).

THE HEART FACE   A heart-shaped face is one in which the top of the head is wider and the chin portion narrower than the rest of the face. To counterbalance this imbalance, select a frame that is heavier on the bottom, as this will bring some of the weight down toward the lower half of your face. If your heart-shaped face is also long, choose a rectangular frame; it will help cut the length.

THE PEAR FACE   Also called the inverted heart shape, the thickness in this face shape is at the bottom, from the jaw through the chin area. In order to balance this out, choose glasses with broad rims to help widen the top portion of your face. Do not wear rimless or thin-metal frames, as these will underscore the natural disproportion of the pear shape.

THE SQUARE FACE   This face is characterized by squared-off angles in the jaw line and a sometimes angular brow area. Look for a softer, more rounded frame that will cut down on the natural angularity of your face. Be sure the outside corners of the frame extend out over your cheekbone, as this cuts the width of the jaw line and makes your face appear more oval.

THE ROUND FACE   Since this face does not usually have angles, you need to choose a frame that will give your face a slightly more angular look. Avoid any frames with harsh, exaggerated angles, as they mix with round faces about as well as oil and water do. Also avoid roundish frames; they will only accentuate the round fullness of your face.

CORRECT FRAME SIZE CHECKLIST

Your frame is too large if:

- too much of the frame extends beyond your eyes on the sides
- too much flesh shows through under the eyes
- you can see your eyebrows through the lens (the frame should completely cover over your brows)
  - the bridge of the frame doesn't fit securely on your nose
  - your glasses slide off when you bend your head forward

Your frame is too small if:

- the outside edges of the frame falls somewhere within the eye area
  - your eyes aren't centered in the frame
  - your eyes are cut off by the frame
  - your eyebrows extend above the frame
  - your eyes overpower your glasses

It's a good idea to consult a reputable eye practitioner (optometrist, optician, or ophthalmologist) whenever you're choosing new frames. Many women purchase high-fashion frames in retail stores or boutiques because they love the way they look, only to discover when they bring them to the optician to be fitted with lenses that the frames aren't suitable to their prescription. Often, an oversized frame will distort a prescription lens, making the glasses unusable. And many frames cannot successfully accommodate very thick lenses. Remember, the reason you wear glasses is to be able to see, so make sure the frame you choose can accommodate your prescription.

WHAT "TEMPLE" PIECES DO   Temple pieces are the arms of the glasses that extend from the lenses straight back and around your ears. Temple pieces have been in the fashion spotlight recently, now that the classic position of the temple piece in the center of the frame has shifted to the top of the frame or even to the bottom. The positioning of these arms, though they will not affect the shape of your face, *can* make a difference in the way your glasses look:

Top temples tend to add a "lift" to the entire face and are especially good if your skin sags or your face tends to "droop."

Center temples are the most common position. A centered temple that is fairly wide will cleverly attract attention *away* from the thickness of a lens.

Bottom temples, especially wide ones, are the newest fashion rage because they tend to camouflage crows-feet and lines that appear at the sides of the eye area.

Color and Eyeglasses

Color in eyeglass fashion comes two ways: in the *frame* and in the *lens.* One color, two-color, and even three-color combinations are used in frames and glass tints alike and can be as dramatic as you want them to be. Eyewear color gives you options you never had before and the chance to express yourself, change your mood, accent your image.

FRAME COLOR

If you stop for a moment to consider that eyeglasses are really accessories, you'll realize how absurd it is that most women who wear glasses still cling to the old-fashioned notion that all they need is one all-purpose frame color. Think about it. You wouldn't wear a delicate cocktail dress with a pair of heavy tortoise-shell glasses, nor would you enter the dining room at your tennis club wearing your sneakers. Yet many women do precisely this by wearing the same glasses morning, noon, and even night.

Almost all modern eyeglass frames come in a wide range of fashion colors, so when you select your frame, look for contrast and interest. Avoid washed-out, fade-away colors that disappear into your face. After all, if you're going to wear glasses you might as well flaunt them—in style. Color has turned eyewear into fashion wear. As with any other accessory or cosmetic, learn what looks and works best on you. The following simple chart will help you to coordinate frame color to both your hair color and complexion.

HAIR COLOR/COMPLEXION	FRAMES	
	"Yes" Colors	*"No" Colors*
Blonde hair/Fair skin:	Taupe, blues, sable, mauve, lilac, tortoise-shell, gold and bronze metal	Pearl or light crystalline tones, yellows
Brunette hair/Fair skin:	Peach, blue, plum, copper	Dark tones of any color
Brunette hair/Dark skin:	Silver, copper, blue, burgundy, gold, pink	Dark tones of any color, especially brown or black
Red hair/Ruddy skin:	Blue, pink, silver, plum, burgundy, gold	Brown, rose, taupe, mauve, lilac
Gray hair/Any skin tone:	Blue, black, pink, silver, metal-gray	Pale crystal tones, yellows

Remember, if you don't see what you're looking for immediately, don't settle! Your eyes are too crucial to your appearance to accept anything that's not the best. Keep looking and you'll find exactly what you want.

LENS COLOR

Colored or tinted lenses are a product of today's innovative technology, and with their invention come not only terrific fashion options but also solutions to many cosmetic dilemmas facing busy women. Colored lenses are the answer for women who can't take the time early in the morning to put on eye makeup yet have to go out and face the world. Tinted glasses, though certainly no substitute for eye makeup, add a dimension of beauty to an otherwise naked eye.

Ideally, you should try to coordinate lens color with frame color, depending on the effect you're trying to create. For example, red frames look smashing with some tinted lenses but look dreadful with green lenses.

WHAT TINTED LENSES WILL DO FOR YOUR EYES

Tinted lenses will:

- enhance the eye in the same way eye makeup does
- hide and minimize the prescription in the lens, especially when the glass is extremely thick
- camouflage the bifocal line many women dislike because it's ``age-telling.'' Several ``lineless'' bifocal progressive-power lenses are now available; however, though they do eliminate the bifocal line, they are quite expensive. Tinted lenses offer a practical, economic solution to this problem.
- play up the color of the frame by emphasizing it. A black frame, for example, looks twice as dramatic with a tinted lens as it does with a clear lens.

THE DEGREE AND TYPE OF TINTING   Tints are graded on a scale from 1 to 5, with 5 being the darkest and the one most often used in sunglasses. Tinting is also available in several forms:

- *solid tints,* which have the same degree of color throughout.
- *gradient tints,* where the tint may be darker on the top or bottom of the lens
- *multi-colored tints,* which can combine two or three colors in one lens

TINTS FOR DAY WEAR   It's best to wear a *gradient tint* rather than a solid tint. The darker top portions are much more dramatic and will highlight your eye makeup and eye shadow. *Blue, bronze,* and *mauve tones* are particularly fashionable as are shades of *rose.* However, if you choose a rose tone, be sure that the rose color is well graded from dark rose to light; otherwise, your eyes will take on a too-pink cast and may appear sickly. Avoid light gray tints because they tend to look drab and will bring out tired lines. Another unflattering shade for most women is light green; unless it's combined with another color, it tends to turn your complexion sallow. Greens and grays are best when used in sunglasses.

TINTS FOR EVENING WEAR   *Tri-tinted lenses* are a knock-out, especially when the color combination is subtle. One of the best trios for night is a *mauve top/blue center/rose bottom*. The mauve on top will enhance your eye shadow underneath; the blue (or green) in the center is a cool color and will draw your eyes out, making the whites look even whiter; the rose (or peach) on the bottom hides and masks any circles or dark shadows and tends to minimize bagginess.

NOTE: *Tri-tinted lenses are also great for correcting eye-proportion problems because the shading can be placed where you need it, just as with corrective makeup. For example, if your eyes are wide-set, you can "bring them together" by wearing lenses that are darker around the edges, thereby creating the effect that your eyes are closer together than they really are.*

Other Facts About Eyeglasses

TYPES OF EYEGLASS LENSES

All eyeglass lenses must be made from impact-resistant glass or plastic. However, since there are so many varieties of lenses on the market, you need to understand what each does and how they differ from each other in order to choose what's best for your needs.

GLASS VERSUS PLASTIC   Each has its own merits. One school of thought claims glass filters out more of the sun's ultra-violet rays than plastic. Yet plastic is lighter than glass and, especially with the large frames so popular today, will be considerably more comfortable. On the other hand, plastic scratches more easily than glass. Which you should choose depends on what you plan to use your glasses for.

PHOTOTROPIC LENSES   These are special, light-sensitive lenses that change from an almost clear color to a dark tint depending on their exposure to different light conditions. They are exceptionally attractive and are great for sports like tennis and skiing, where the outdoor light conditions constantly change.

POLARIZING LENSES   These lenses are specially designed to help reduce glare and are ideal for use when skiing, boating, or anywhere there is tremendous reflection. For intense glare, mirrored lenses are best.

GRADIENT-DENSITY LENSES   This type of lens is made darker on top and makes a good choice for driving and boating.

EYEGLASS COST

Many women never question spending a hundred dollars or more on the "perfect" accessory, yet all too often the same women skimp when it comes to buying eyeglasses. Just think about how this kind of counter-productive economics can undermine an investment. You can have the most polished makeup, the most magnificent hairdo, the most elegant clothes and destroy the entire image with the wrong eyeglasses. Far worse, you can even damage your precious vision by wearing shoddily made eyeglasses. Glasses are a key part of your total look and deserve to be of the same quality as every other important accessory in your wardrobe.

EYEGLASS CARE

Since a good pair of eyeglasses is likely to represent a substantial investment, for most women protecting and caring for them is not only sound hygiene, it's an economic necessity.

• Keep glasses clean by washing them daily in a soap-and-warm-water solution. Wipe dry with a soft tissue. If they are extra greasy from facial oils or makeup, wipe them with an ammonia-based cleaner before you wash them in soap and water.
• Never put your glasses on a surface with the lenses facing down as this is a sure way to scratch them.
• Have your glasses adjusted periodically and get them repaired immediately if parts are broken or missing.
• Always carry your glasses in a hard case. Hard cases give much better protection—especially in your handbag—than soft ones.

Special-Use Glasses and Contact Lenses

SUNGLASSES

Sunglasses are a special breed of eye wear and a must for every fashionable woman. Sunglasses are truly a *necessity*, not just a luxury. They not only protect the eyes from the sun's harmful rays but also help eliminate squinting, which, over a period of years, will certainly cause lines and wrinkling.

The single most important thing to look for in choosing sunglasses is the color and quality of the lens. Always buy the best quality you can afford. Also, keep in mind that according to eye specialists, sunglasses should never allow more than 30 percent of the natural light to pass through the glass. For use at the beach or where there's snow, sunglasses should block out all but 10 to 15 percent of natural light. Check before you buy.

RECREATIONAL GLASSES

These are a must for any sports activity in which your eyes run the risk of being damaged. Sports like racket ball, tennis, squash, baseball, hockey, swimming, even do-it-yourself projects, leave the eyes vulnerable to injury. To protect your eyes adequately requires the use of special eye guards—a sports eye protector or industrial safety lenses. *Industrial-quality safety glasses* come with either non-corrective lenses or lenses ground to your prescription. These glasses should have plastic lenses and bear the insignia Z87.1, 1979, indicating that they meet the current requirements of the American National Standard Practice for Occupational and Educational Eye and Face Protection. *Sports eye protectors*, which are goggle-type molded eye guards, with or without lenses, are also made with prescription lenses. They can be purchased from opticians and at sporting goods stores.

CONTACT LENSES

There are many types of contact lenses available, including the original hard lens, the new soft lens, a combination hard/soft lens, even a bifocal lens. Hard lenses can be tinted so that they seem to change the color of your eyes; soft lenses, which are made of a gel, are not as readily impregnated with color and the tint gradually loses its effectiveness.

Contact lenses are great adjuncts to your eyeglass wardrobe and you owe it to yourself to try them as an alternative to glasses. There are some situations where glasses are simply not practical, especially in sports, and contact lenses give you the option you need.

If you do wear contacts, don't put them in or remove them in public. Wait until you're alone and can do it in private. Beside looking a little odd, you run the risk of losing your tiny lenses in your soup, on the rug, and so on. Changing contacts in public is also highly unsanitary and the transfer of bacteria to the eyes can cause any number of serious eye disorders.

SPECIAL EYE MAKEUP TIPS FOR CONTACT LENS WEARERS

If the reason you wear contacts is to make your eyes look more beautiful, you need to apply eye makeup with your contacts in mind. Here are a few common-sense tips that will improve and simplify your eye makeup routine.

• Put in your lenses *before* you apply your eye makeup; otherwise, you'll smear and smudge that polished look you spent precious time creating. Also, there's the chance that your eyes will tear a bit as you position the lenses and this, too, will mess your eye makeup.

• Use a water-soluble mascara so that if small particles of it get into your eyes they will dissolve quickly with little or no irritation.

• Avoid lash-lengthening mascaras that are formulated with fibers. The fibers can easily get into your eyes and cause problems.

• For color and highlighting, use pencils instead of loose powders, as they are less likely to flake into the eyes. You can also use a pressed powder, but be sure to dampen it before applying.

• Line the inside of your eyes with kajal, but be sure to check the product you use. It should be specially formulated for safe use inside the eye.

• Apply all eye makeup with a soft brush. Never use your fingers as they will exert too much pressure and can cause your lenses to pop out.

• Always remove your lenses before cleansing your eyes of makeup. Rubbing can cause irritation and also scratch the lens surface.

Eye Makeup and Eyeglasses

Even without glasses, your eyes are the focal point of your face. Eyewear *guarantees* that your eyes will become an even more dominant feature. Eyeglasses, especially tinted ones, tend to minimize and "drown out" your eyes and your eye makeup so your objective when making up your eyes should be to use a slightly more pronounced eye makeup that will enhance and bring out your eyes. Following these simple hints will help you maximize what you've got:

- Always use a bit more eye shadow than normal. This will give greater definition and shape to the eye.
- Use deep-toned eye shadows, as eyewear camouflages eye makeup color. For example, if you normally wear a medium blue shadow, use a dark to navy blue shadow instead.
- Use a smudge-proof mascara that contains no fibers. Avoid waterproof and lash-thickening mascaras; they tend to dry out and flake into the eyes and onto the lenses.
- Use enough mascara so your lashes make a distinctive rim around the eye. This creates a better balance between the eye and the frame of the glasses.
- Rim inside your lower and upper lids with black kajal to emphasize the whites of your eyes. Otherwise, they tend to get lost behind the glasses.
- Use a strong highlighter color in an iridescent rather than a matte form, even for daytime. Iridescent highlighting will shimmer through the glasses as opposed to a matte highlighter which may scarcely show up. Highlighter is a *must* for women who wear glasses, as it adds depth to the eye and helps pull the shape of the eye through the glasses.
- Don't forget to use liner. It helps create the impression of a thicker lash line. For most women black liner is best.
- Shade under the lower lash line with a deep, neutral shade (gray, black, navy, dark brown, eggplant). Smudge the color to create a hazy effect. This will soften the eye as well as the shape of the eyeglass frame and help bring the focus of attention to your eye rather than your glasses.
- Groom your brows as you would if you did not wear glasses. Since the top of your glass frame should be directly on top of where

your eyebrows are, your brows will not be visible and so do not need special treatment.

Eyeglass Guidelines

The skillful interplay between eyes and eyeglasses can result in a beautiful look you never dreamed possible. So practice, experiment, and play with shape, style, and color and the partnership will pay the best beauty dividend possible. Once you've mastered the following do's and don'ts, you will be able to wear eyeglasses fashionably and attractively. Remember that painful quote Dorothy Parker made famous: "Men seldom make passes at girls who wear glasses?" Well, my reply to that is, "Not true." Women who wear glasses have come a long way. So watch out men. Women who wear glasses will turn your head!

1. When selecting glasses evaluate your face shape. The basic premise here is to try to draw attention toward your eyes and away from the least attractive part of your face. Look at the five face shapes in this chapter (pages 90–91) and you'll see how frame shapes can help correct face-shape problems.

2. Try to achieve a balance between your features by selecting a frame that's in proportion to your face. If your face is small, for example, don't overpower it with oversized glasses.

3. Decide what you're going to be using your glasses for and choose from the many different styles and types accordingly.

4. Coordinate frame and lens color to the color of your hair and the tone of your skin as well as your wardrobe. Eye color is no longer an important factor when choosing lenses as most lenses today are tinted and create their own illusion of color.

5. When applying eye makeup to be worn under glasses remember that glasses and frames tend to drown out your eyes. Emphasize your eyes by using a slightly more pronounced eye makeup including liner and plenty of mascara.

6. Glasses shouldn't fight eyebrows and vice versa. One pair of eyebrows is sufficient for any woman, so be sure the frames cover your own brows completely. Avoid that "dragon lady" look with pointy, peaked brows that conflict with every frame style.

7. Build a wardrobe of glasses for different seasons, occasions, fashion looks, color palettes, etc.

8. If you wear hats, be sure they coordinate with your eyeglasses. A tiny pillbox won't work with heavy tortoise-shell frames any more than wire-framed aviator glasses will look right under your summer straw hat. Watch for scale and proportion. They should be in sync.

As for hats with veils, I'm all for any woman who likes to play *femme fatale* for a day, but keep the occasion in mind. If you do opt for a veil, don't do it for your next luncheon meeting or anyplace where you'll be eating and smoking.

9. Never slide your glasses up onto the top of your head. It ruins the shape of your frames, scratches the lenses, and spoils your hairdo.

10. Don't wear chains on glasses. It's dated and will add years to your image. If you need to wear glasses all the time, far better to invest in a stylish pair of bifocals.

11. If you dislike or are uncomfortable wearing glasses all the time but have no choice, try lorgnettes. Lorgnettes are magnificent pieces of jewelry. If you like to hunt in antique shops and flea markets you can find some real beauties at bargain prices and then have them refitted with your own prescription lenses. Lorgnettes can be used with great flourish and drama and, if you're the nervous type socially, they give you something to do with your hands.

10 / Eye and Beauty Pharmacopoeia

Beauty is a promise of happiness.
— STENDHAL

THOUGH DEPARTMENT STORES and drugstores line their shelves with cosmetic potions and bottled beauty, it's still great fun to tap your own creative resources and brew up a batch of a fabulous tonic, lotion or cream and label it as your own. Over the years I have collected, tried, and tested a variety of interesting do-it-yourself beauty recipes, many of which I have found to be extraordinarily effective. In part, this is because I prefer beauty concoctions that use natural ingredients and rely heavily on herbs, fruits, and vegetables. You can find most everything you need for the recipes in this chapter in your local market or health food store.

One of the most imaginative gifts you can give friends and family is a package of these beauty recipes. I like to buy antique or interestingly shaped jars and bottles and then fill them with a particularly pretty beauty potion. As a finishing touch, I label the jars with a design I've created and hand-lettered. Once you begin giving these beauty recipes as gifts, I guarantee you'll have a long reorder list and your gift-giving worries for your friends will be over. Incidentally, don't leave out men from your gift-giving list! Men, just as much as women—and sometimes I think even *more*—love to feel pampered. You'll be surprised at how flattered that special man will be.

NOTE: *Though some of these concoctions sound delicious enough to eat, please don't! Except where specifically indicated, they are intended to be applied externally and not ingested.*

Eye Moisturizers

Home-made eye moisturizers are made primarily of creams or oils and are exceptionally effective when used on those tiny lines that have a way of making their nest around the eyes. (I have never understood why women sometimes call these lines crow's-feet. I prefer to call them "expression" lines, as they are a beautiful evidence of the emotions and experiences—both good and bad—a woman has as she goes through life. In fact, I have become quite fond of mine.)

All women—regardless of age and skin type—need a good moisturizer around the eye area. Because eyes are thin-skinned and don't have their own natural lubricating mechanism—that is, a layer of fat beneath the dermis—they need all the moisturizing help they can get. *Your eyes need to be moisturized every day.* I find the morning the best time to apply a cream or oil, since applying it at night and going to bed with it on can lead to puffy eyes in the morning. However, this is not necessarily true for all women so I suggest you do what works best for you. Ideally, you should try to leave your eye moisturizer on for thirty minutes to an hour. This can be perfectly managed, even in the busiest schedule, if you apply your moisturizer in the morning and then sit down to relax with your coffee and paper before starting the day. By the time you are finished reading, your skin will have soaked in the lubrication and you'll feel refreshed and eager to get going. Be sure to wipe off any last trace of moisturizer *before* applying your eye makeup or everything will smear off.

OLIVE OIL SOAK

You may remember that Gloria Swanson performed this little trick in the movie *Sunset Boulevard.* Though it's not guaranteed to turn you into a Hollywood star, it is extremely effective. I suggest you do this one when you're alone.

Warm some olive oil in a pan. While it's heating, cut two cotton strips that are small enough to fit under the eyes. Soak them in the warm olive oil and then place them under each eye. Gently secure in place with adhesive tape or by some other means. Leave them on as long as you wish. Following this regime each morning or evening will also help minimize dark circles, swellings, and puffiness and even reduce fatigue signs around the eyes. But, of course, the best effect of the olive oil is its wonderful moisturizing magic.

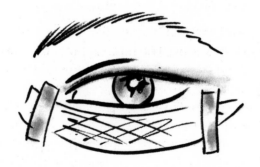

Vitamin E Oil

This is a super-simple recipe because vitamin E by itself is a very effective eye moisturizer. You can buy oil in a bottle or in a capsule form which you break open to release the oil. Dab it around the eye area with your fingertip. I am such a firm believer in vitamin E that I also take a 400mg vitamin E supplement at breakfast and again before going to sleep.

Carrot Eye Oil

Cut up one carrot and place it in a blender, food processor, or juicer. Add enough safflower oil to the pulp to create a creamy consistency (not too thin or it will run off your face). Apply it gently around the eye area.

Madeleine's Own Home-Made Eye Cream

There is a great sense of satisfaction in making your very own eye cream. This one will help keep the eye area soft and lubricated. But remember, eyes are extremely delicate and if you are prone to allergies, take extra care whenever you use any special cream around your eyes. Here are the ingredients for my own special cream:

> 3 tablespoons Anhydrous lanolin (solid or liquid)
> 1 tablespoon mineral oil
> 1 egg yolk
> 2 tablespoons beeswax
> 2 tablespoons safflower oil
> 1 tablespoon cold water (optional)

Melt the lanolin and mineral oil together in the top of a double boiler until the mixture gels a little. The mineral oil helps cleanse eye makeup from your eyes, but you can substitute another tablespoon of lanolin for the oil if you prefer. Add the beaten egg yolk to the mixture. In another double boiler, melt the beeswax and safflower oil. Add this mixture to the lanolin, mineral oil, and egg yolk. Add a drop or two of water if you wish, as this helps blend everything together. Beat the mixture until frothy. When the mixture cools, pour into a pretty jar and store in the refrigerator until you're ready to use it. Apply as you would your regular moisturizer.

Eye Tonics

One money-saving tip before we start. Many of these recipes include eye pads and there is a very economical way of always keeping a plentiful supply on hand. Buy a roll of surgical cotton wool, the kind that is layered and then wrapped in blue paper in a "Swiss" roll. It is available in most drugstores and is the cheapest variety of 100 percent cotton. (It is important to use only pure cotton as this remarkable substance is the best nonirritant for sensitive skin.) To make your eye pads, simply unroll enough cotton to cut a row of squares 2½" × 2½". Cut up fifty or sixty squares at a time and keep them in a pretty pot or apothecary jar for later use.

"Sweet Dreams" Cider 'n' Honey

There's nothing better for tired eyes than a good night's sleep. Years ago I was curious enough to try an old New England folk medicine brew that promised to produce a restful night of sleep. Skeptical as I was, I tried it and it worked. I've been sipping the brew ever since. It may have the same wonderful effect on you. Here's how to find out: Mix 2 teaspoons of apple cider vinegar into ½ cup of honey. Shake well. Place the mixture in a glass jar (a honey bottle is ideal) and keep in a handy location near your bed. If you take one or two teaspoons before you go to bed, you should be fast asleep within half an hour. If, by the end of an hour, you are not asleep, take another teaspoon or two of the mixture. In cases of extreme wakefulness, you may need several such doses and if you should awake during the night and feel unable to get back to sleep, you should take still another dose. This is far better and healthier than taking any "lullaby pills" because it is a treatment based on nature's own infallible knowledge of bodily requirements. And because the honey and cider mixture is safe, you can use this remedy indefinitely. Honey is a natural sedative and may also be taken by itself; combining it with apple cider vinegar, however, is more effective.

Chamomile Compress

Chamomile tea has long been known for its beneficial effect on the skin. Make a brew of chamomile tea with 1 part chamomile to 3 parts boiling water. Let cool. Soak cotton pads in this mixture and place on your eyes. Leave in place for 10 to 15 minutes. The pads are wonderful for relieving any inflammation or puffiness.

TEA BAG TONIC

Wet 2 tea bags and place one on each eye. Stretch out for 10 minutes and let the leaves take away puffiness and unsightly dark circles.

CUCUMBER COOLER

This one is a snap and especially good to use after you've spent the day at the beach and return home with eyes that are a bit tired or strained from the sun. Slice a chilled cucumber into thin rounds. Place one round on each eye and leave in place for 15 minutes. Remove and gently splash your eyes with cool water. You'll find it wonderfully refreshing.

POTATO PASTE

Grate 1 potato in a blender or food processor. Apply the paste around the eyes and over the lids. Leave on for 10 to 15 minutes or enough time to allow the mixture to soak into the skin. While you're resting it will help smooth tired and delicate eye tissue.

WITCH HAZEL MAGIC

Witch hazel has a thousand and one uses and I never travel without a small bottle of this magical liquid. History tells us that the American Indians made potions from the witch hazel plant and used them for soothing bruises. The cooling and healing powers were quickly appreciated by the English settlers, who in turn introduced the seeds of the plant to England in the eighteenth century.

To use witch hazel as an eye tonic, simply pour a small amount directly onto cotton pads, or use cotton pads that have been slightly moistened with cool water, and place the pads over your eyes for 10 to 15 minutes. This will help reduce tiredness and puffiness. Store the witch hazel in the refrigerator as it feels even more refreshing when it is icy cold.

HELP FOR A BLACK EYE

Chances are you may never get a black eye, but accidents do happen. Being one of the unfortunates, this is what I did for mine:

Grate a yellow apple (it must be yellow, *not* red or green) and make a compress by placing the grated apple between two square pieces of clean, soft cotton cloth or gauze. Apply to your eye. The swelling should soon reduce and disappear.

BEE STING ICER

If you get bitten by a bee or mosquito or any other insect, immediately apply ice that has been wrapped in gauze or cloth to the affected area. This will reduce the swelling and itchiness. Be careful never to apply ice directly to the thin eye skin or you'll get a case of frostbite that's far more serious than the bee sting.

RED-EYE REMEDY

If your eyes develop redness and irritation, gently place one drop of castor oil in your eye with an eye dropper. The oil will help relieve the irriation and make the eye feel more comfortable.

EYELID LIFT

Sometimes, the rims of eyelids may become scaly or granulated due to a nutritional deficiency, allergic reaction, or simply tiredness. If this happens to your eyes, take 1 teaspoon of corn oil each morning at breakfast and again at the evening meal. Within one month, this unsightly condition should disappear.

Healthy-Eye Drinks

Some kind friends brought me a juice extractor as a gift. Ever since I have been making the most wonderfully healthy drinks and have discovered some for the benefit of eyes. Most extractors come with instructions on the amounts of various vegetables it takes to make an eight-ounce glass of juice. All you need to do is feed the vegetables into the extractor and the processed liquid comes out ready to drink—in seconds. So here are some health drinks I've tried and pass on to you. Please don't expect them to work miracles. They are just marvelously healthful brews that will help keep you at your peak. Try to drink at least one glass of a vegetable juice every day.

CARROT JUICE

We all know that story about rabbits being able to see in the dark. Well, maybe it's an old wives' tale, but my husband, who is older than I am (naturally), says the story got started during World War II when the Allied pilots were given radar. In order to account for the high success rate of their missions, the story was released that the pilots were fed carrots to enable them to see in the dark. The cover story was spread to keep the German forces from learning about the technological breakthrough too soon. True or not, we all associate carrots with healthy eyes and good vision, especially because they're high in vitamin A, a vitamin which nutritionists have shown is indeed beneficial to the eyes—besides its benefits to hair and skin. Try a glass of carrot juice today!

ENDIVE JUICE

Endives, in addition to making a delicious salad, are often recommended for weak or tired eyes. They are extremely high in vitamins A, C, and G and also provide a good supply of potassium, sodium, chlorine, and calcium. Put some in your juicer next time you feel adventurous. Endive juice is good for you and tastes good, too!

SPINACH JUICE

Spinach probably would have made news even without Popeye's help because it is a rich source of vitamins A, E, and G, as well as that all-important mineral, iron. It is recommended for the correction of glandular disturbances, obesity (spinach juice has only 115 calories per pint), and last, but not least, weak eyes.

Eyewashes

A gentle eyewash, when used sparingly (they can disturb the natural film that covers, protects, and lubricates the eye), will cleanse, tone, and clear red and irritated eyes.

MINT TEA EYEWASH

Mint is a stimulating, refreshing herb and an effective beauty aid. Brew a pot or cup of mint tea and dilute it with water (3 parts water to 1 part tea). Use with an eyecup to give your eyes a refreshing pick-up.

SALT EYEWASH

Dissolve about ¼ teaspoon of table salt in 1 cup warm water. Pour solution in an eyecup and bathe your eyes.

CITRUS SQUIRT EYEWASH

I pass this one on to you for fun since I wouldn't use it for love or money. Once you've been met in the eye with any variety of citrus fruit juice, you get a little touchy about using the fruit for any purpose other than eating. But there were a few stalwart ladies of the eighteenth century who nonchalantly squeezed citrus juice into their eyes to make them sparkle. My advice: Drink it instead.

Optical Illusions

No matter how beautiful your eyes may be, there are some days when you're going to need a bit of trickery to help fool the world. Here are some of my favorite "foolers" you may want to try.

EYE-WHITE WONDER

This treatment is especially effective when you are going to be photographed and you know you don't look your very best. Though this is only a temporary measure and may be a bit messy to use, it's definitely worth the trouble as it instantly smooths wrinkles and relieves puffiness under the eyes.

Take an unbeaten egg white and, using your fingertip or a small, soft brush, gently apply it in very thin layers to the skin above and underneath your eyes. Let it dry. The egg white will pull the skin taut just enough for it to appear less saggy. Now very gently, so as not to disturb the coating, apply foundation cream and your other makeup. The egg white is invisible on your skin but the effect lasts for hours.

SAGE TEA EYEBROW DYE

Brew some very strong sage tea and then brush it onto your eyebrows. This is an effective, natural way to darken the brows.

Parsley Perk-Up

If you want to soothe your sun- or pollution-irritated eyes, try this natural treatment.

Chop ½ cup fresh parsley (ideally in a wooden bowl) until the juice from the leaves and stems appears. Place the chopped parsley and the juice into an old handkerchief or piece of clean, soft cloth. Fold the material several times and tie with string to secure. Dip the parsley sack in hot water for a few seconds. (This helps release more of its healthful juices.) Gently press the sack to your eyes. Leave on until it cools. If necessary, repeat in an hour.

Eyelash Lengthener

This remarkable recipe, which will actually help you to grow your eyelashes, was taught to me by Nana Alice, my maternal grandmother.

Scented Castor Oil

Insert a thin slice of lemon or orange peel into a 1-ounce bottle of castor oil. (The lemon peel adds a lovely bit of scent.) Use your fingertip to apply the oil to your upper and lower lashes every night. Be sure to cover all the lashes completely, gently stroking them from the root out to the tips. Don't expect overnight miracles, but this little trick will keep your lashes looking lustrous. And because they'll be healthier, they *will* begin to grow. Castor oil lasts indefinitely, so this tip is also quite economical.

Garden Cosmetics

Now that your eyes look great, why not try adding extra sparkle to them by making other parts of your body feel great as well! Here are a few sensations from my special recipe file for general beauty care—face and hands, especially.

FOR THE FACE

ELDER FLOWER FRESHENER

Women have used this recipe to keep their skin looking fresh since the nineteenth century. Place 3 tablespoons tincture of benzoin and ¾ cup elder-flower water in a tight-lidded jar. Gently pat your face with this mixture as needed. It is purely and simply the best cooling refresher a woman can ever apply to her face.

"IDAHO RUB"

The potato has surprisingly beneficial cleansing and drawing properties, so why not take full advantage of this remarkable plant? Cut an Idaho potato in half. Wash it very carefully, trying not to bruise it, and then rub it all over your face or wherever you have skin blemishes. It will absorb dead skin and coax out hidden grime that simple washing cannot get out. Use this technique to supplement your normal cleansing routine.

ROSE TONIC

Roses, in addition to being one of the most beautiful garden flowers, are also effective when used in skin tonics. Here's a flowery, rose-water recipe to dab on your face anytime your skin needs a quick and refreshing pick-up.

Collect enough rose petals to equal 2 pounds. Place 3 cups of petals in a saucepan, preferably one made out of heat-resistant glass. Barely cover them with cold water to prevent scalding and cook gently over a very low flame for about 45 minutes. Carefully spoon out the cooked petals from the pan (leaving the water) and place 3 more cups of fresh petals into the pan. Don't add more water. Repeat until the 2 pounds of petals have been cooked. The liquid is now ready to be strained through cheesecloth into an apothecary jar. Do not use the tonic until the liquid has "rested" for several days.

For a refreshingly cool tonic, you can store the mixture in the refrigerator, although it will keep anywhere. Dab on with a cotton ball.

WRINKLE ERASER

Soak geranium leaves in rose water (see preceding recipe) and place them whole on your face. This recipe is renowned for softening the skin and erasing wrinkles. Of course, you have to lie in a prone position to do this effectively—which also helps give you a bit of a rest.

APRICOT ANTI-WRINKLE CREAM

Apricots are rich in vitamin A and their oil is very fine and nourishing.

> 2 tablespoons lanolin
> 2 tablespoons almond oil
> 1 tablespoon apricot oil
> 1 tablespoon lemon juice
> Perfume oil

Melt the lanolin and oils together and add in the lemon juice and perfume oil. When the cream is cool, give it a final whip and you will have about ¾ cup of elegant, rich, anti-wrinkle cream.

SOUTH SEA ISLAND CREAM

In the South Seas and all over South America and India, coconut oil is very widely used. Although it is hard, it has a low melting point; it melts on touching the skin or when in the sun, which gives this cream a very fine consistency. Even the name of this cream makes me feel good!

> 3 tablespoons coconut oil
> 2 tablespoons olive oil
> 1 tablespoon almond oil
> 1½ teaspoons beeswax
> 3½ tablespoons hot water
> ½ teaspoon borax
> Perfume oil

Melt the oils and beeswax together in a double boiler. Remove from heat and slowly add the hot water in which you have dissolved the borax. Stir until cool and the mixture will gradually become a pure-white soft cream. This recipe will yield about ¾ cup of fabulous cream. I like to add a few drops of my favorite jasmine oil, which gives the cream a lovely scent, but you can add any perfume oil to give the cream your own exclusive fragrance. Use as you would any moisturizer.

Marigold Lotion

If you love the brilliant gold and orange colors of these pungent and delightful garden blooms, you'll be glad to learn about the beauty assets of marigolds, the mucilage of which is said to be very beneficial for cleansing and clearing the skin of eczema, spots, and grease. Steam marigold leaves in boiling water and let cool for up to three hours. Strain, and dab the solution on your face.

Honey 'n' Egg Facial Mask

Combine the white of an egg, 1 teaspoon of fat-free dry milk, and a ½ teaspoon honey. Beat with a fork until the mixture is blended. Cleanse your face as usual. Now, apply the mask in a thick layer all over your face and throat area. Leave on for 20 minutes while you rest. Remove with tepid water, then rinse again with ice water. Your skin will feel refreshed and smooth.

FOR THE HANDS

Honey Hand Lotion

This fabulous mixture can be made in minutes. Blend together ¼ cup each of lemon juice, your favorite cologne, and honey. Put the mixture into a small bottle, shake well, and refrigerate. Apply a small amount to your hands every morning and evening or whenever they feel dry. A little goes a long way, so rub in well.

"Take-Away" Lotion

This lotion is great for ridding hands of onion, garlic, or other annoying smells. It's also a good bleaching agent for freckles and spots. Combine 2 tablespoons glycerin and 2 tablespoons lemon juice and shake well. Apply to hands as needed.

POTATO PAMPER

I've always had a passion for potatoes, but my diet doctor says they're taboo. Since I did not want to cut them out of my life altogether, I began to use this concoction which I once read was an old plantation secret used by Southern belles to keep their hands delicate and lily white.

Boil 2 potatoes in their skins until you can pierce them through with a fork. Peel and mash. Gradually add 1 teaspoon each of sweet almond oil and glycerine until the mixture is a smooth soft paste. Apply to your hands and cover with cotton gloves. Now relax and read or take a nap. When you've rested, remove gloves and rinse off your hands with warm water.

MAYO MAGIC

Thoroughly massage a liberal quantity of mayonnaise into your hands. (The store-bought variety is fine; home-made mayonnaise is even better.) Put on a pair of cotton gloves to "seal" in the mayonnaise. You'll be surprised at the results. (This is a good tip for night care; the gloves will keep the bed linens tidy.)

FOR THE HAIR

INDIAN HAIR CONDITIONER

Indian women have long been admired for their beautiful, shiny hair—as well as for their eyes. When their hair is dried out from the hot sun, this is what they do to condition their hair and restore the luster: Mix equal amounts of peanut flour, lemon juice, and plain yogurt. (Peanut flour can be found in health food stores or you can grind up your own peanuts. The aroma is divine!) Work the mixture through your dry hair. Leave on for 5 minutes. Wash your hair twice with your regular shampoo to remove every trace of conditioner. Follow with a vinegar rinse for a fabulous shine.

GERANIUM HAIR RINSE

I really know summer has arrived when I look out the window and see wonderful pots of colorful geraniums. When I feel like spoiling myself, this is what I do:

Shampoo your hair and use conditioner. Do not dry. Now, pour 3 or 4 cups of boiling water over approximately ½ cup of geranium flowers. Steep the blossoms like tea leaves for about 20 minutes. The liquid should now be cool. Strain it, discard the flowers, and use as a rinse over your hair. Do not rinse off this heavenly scented brew. It will give your hair a lovely allure.

FOR THE BODY

EXOTIC MASSAGE CREAM

One of the passions of my life is the smell of jasmine. In India, ten days before a girl is to become a bride she is massaged with a special powder mixed with jasmine oil. There are seventeen ingredients in this traditional powder. Unfortunately, most of them are unavailable in this country, so this recipe is the next best thing. Try it, you may like it. Anyway, you'll smell great.

    1 tablespoon orange peel, dried, ground, and sieved
    1 tablespoon lemon peel, dried, ground, and sieved
    2 tablespoons ground almonds, blanched first to remove dark skin
    4 tablespoons wheat germ flour
    1 tablespoon ground thyme
    Pinch of salt
    Pinch of allspice
    Almond oil (enough to make a workable paste)
    Jasmine oil (to perfume to taste)

Combine all ingredients together and blend until they form a smooth cream.

11/Eye Watch

A blemish in the soul cannot be corrected in the face;
but a blemish in the face,
if corrected, can refresh the soul.

— JEAN COCTEAU

EYES, AS THE SENSE ORGANS vital to bringing us a picture of the world at large and in tuning in color, shape, scale, and motion, need all the attention, maintenance, and exercise we can give them. So watching out for the health of our eyes is every bit as important as making them beautiful. When you stop to tally up the many remarkable functions eyes perform, you'll realize why eye care counts so importantly in the overall beauty scheme.

The following helping hints and tips answer many of the questions most often asked by women concerned with eye care and beauty.

Caring for Your Eyes

Many women who live with lifeless, colorless-looking skin spend inordinate amounts of time and energy in their efforts to camouflage the problem with makeup. However, there is another way to treat this condition which is noncosmetic. Dull skin coloration, often thought to be hereditary or the result of too little sleep, can really be caused by the structural quirks of human anatomy. Your head is the highest point on your body and if you understand the basic laws of gravity you'll realize that your blood supply tends to drain from high areas first. In some faces, this will cause a skin tone to look "colorless." Here's a good tip to help stimulate and regain that healthy glow every woman should have:

New "Slant" on Circulation

Many women swear by a slant board, but sometimes I feel like swearing *at* mine, especially when I trip over it. However, it *is* one of the most effective beauty aids I know of. Place your slant board (which can be purchased at any department store) or an ironing board (just as good), on the floor, raising up one end at about a 45-degree angle to the wall. Now lie on the board, completely stretched out with your feet elevated higher than your head. Do this for about 15 minutes daily or at least four or five times a week. This position, similiar to many practiced in yoga, will help increase your circulation and stimulate the blood flow to the head and face, thereby helping to revitalize the dull, drab skin tone of your face. You'll quickly see some rosy-toned cheeks and an overall improvement in your complexion.

Pale-Face to Bright-Eyed . . . In Seconds!

One of the simplest ways of looking better immediately when you feel ill, tired, or are just looking a bit pale is a trick I borrowed from the Japanese bride's traditional wedding makeup: Brush pale pink eye shadow on your eyelids for a delicate, youthful, blushing appearance. If you don't happen to have this particular shade on hand, substitute a pink-toned face blusher. Just a few strokes on your eyelids, and your eyes and face will look healthier and more radiant . . . in seconds!

Help for the Traveling Woman

Women today travel thousands of miles for business and pleasure, and eyes get dehydrated quickly when the moisture level in the plane is extremely low. Because of this excessive dryness, it is advisable to drink plenty of water during and after the flight—at least eight ounces every hour. I always travel with eye drops in my bag which I use before becoming air borne on a long trip. I use them again before landing so my eyes look lubricated and fresh. If you're on an overnight flight, it's a good idea to gently pat on a little eye cream before you board, reapplying it throughout your trip. Make a point of getting off the plane looking as immaculate as when you got on. After all, I'm a firm believer that a woman should be ready (by that I mean well groomed) for anything!

WHY SLEEP ON A PILLOW?

One pillow, two pillows, no pillows, feather pillows, foam pillows—the debate rages on and the preferences are as varied and individual as the heads that lay down to rest. My advice is to always sleep with your head elevated on a comfortable pillow, as this will help eliminate puffy eyes in the morning. If you read in bed, why not try supporting your head with one of those wonderful Chinese neck cushions? I use mine every day and never travel without it.

IF YOU HAVE FACIAL SCARS

The best approach to facial scars is not to camouflage or cover them but to distract attention away from them. Concealing creams and foundation layered over scars only call attention to them. Better to make the most of your eyes with striking makeup. Beautiful eyes will draw attention *away* from your flaws and *toward* the glamorous look you are projecting.

IF YOU'RE A SUNBATHING DEVOTEE

One of the occasions when our eyes need the most protection is when we're in or under the sun. After all, the only layer between the eyeball and the sun's rays is a very, very thin eyelid. Eye specialists tell us that prolonged exposure to sunlight can damage the cornea, causing a temporary reduction in night vision (which may interfere with our ability to drive home safely after a day on the beach). Also, after extended exposure to the sun's ultraviolet rays, you may increase the risk of developing cataracts. The following soothing remedies will help save your precious eyes from any damage:

• Soak two cotton balls with cold water or, better still, some iced tea from your beach thermos. Rest the pads on your eyelids. They'll provide soothing and substantial protection from the sun.

• If you have forgotten both cotton and iced water, try placing a small seashell over each eye instead. (But be sure there's no sand inside!)

• If you find yourself sunning and have no sun protection with you but do have your makeup kit, apply a coat of eye shadow to your lids while sunbathing. Most eye shadow formulations contain some lanolin which provides a layer of protection between your thin lid skin and the sun.

When to Give Your Eyes the Day Off

Once a week you should give your eyes—and the rest of your face—the day off. Turn the mirrors over and take a holiday. Which reminds me of a haunting yet very funny story: A male friend of mine in the midst of getting a divorce told me recently that his wife was so vain, always looking in the mirror of the car, that even now, months after she was out of his life, her face is still reflected in the mirror! I doubt that any of you reading this suffer from such a high degree of vanity. Even so, it's important to give your eyes a day off. Keep your face makeup-free during the day. This allows your skin to rest for at least twelve hours. Just as important, it lets the skin breathe. You can apply a light moisturizer around the delicate eye areas, remembering always to apply moisturizer in light, "up and away" strokes. Apply more moisturizer as it becomes absorbed. What nourishment! Your eyes will love every second of the holiday.

Keeping Your Eyes Healthy

There's no mistaking healthy eyes. They have a special vitality and sparkle. They are clear and alert. They command your attention. Begin with these attributes, and even before you apply eye makeup you'll have a head start on looking beautiful.

How do you keep your eyes healthy? How do you know which remedies are safe and which may be harmful? It's difficult to know for certain if you're not a professional. Sometimes, even the most innocent-seeming actions—from the simple overuse of eye drops to the unthinking use of bacteria-laden eye equipment—can cause a good deal of harm to the eyes and jeopardize their health and safety. The following tips and advice for helping you keep your eyes in top-notch condition come from an expert, Dr. Ira Kaufman of the North Shore Hospital in Long Island and the New York Hospital in New York City.

WHAT TO DO FOR RED, TEARY EYES

The two places no woman wants to ever see red are in her bank book and in her eyes. When the teariness, redness, and irritation in your eyes persist and you know the high pollen count of hayfever season is over, it may be due to a cosmetic allergy. Remove all your eye makeup, face makeup, and nail enamel. Yes, you did read that correctly—nail enamel. Many women who don't wear any eye makeup at all can still reinfect their eyes through contact with the nail enamel on their fingers! So, take all your nail polish off along with the rest of your makeup and after a day or two, when your eyes are feeling better, very gradually begin wearing eye makeup and nail polish again. Add one product at a time until you build back to your full beauty routine. For instance, if you have used mascara for a few days without any ill effect, then start with your eye shadow, kohl, and so on. By this simple process of elimination you will be able to tell which product is the culprit that is disturbing your eyes. If the condition continues, however, be sure to consult with your eye doctor.

WHEN YOU GET SOMETHING IN YOUR EYE

Eye injuries of all kinds require a common first aid treatment—cold water. If a foreign substance gets into your eye, irrigate the eye with cold tap water immediately. Then telephone your doctor to describe the accident and get further advice for how to treat it. If the injury develops into a bruised or black eye, try to apply cold compresses right away. Or you might opt for my effective "yellow apple" remedy (see page 110).

SHOULD YOU USE AN EYEWASH?

The next time you go to a sad movie and have a good cry, in addition to feeling that you got your money's worth, you can go home happy, knowing that your eyes just got a nice spring cleaning—for tears do the job of washing the eyes better than any store-bought remedy.

Apart from sad movies, if you need to wash out your eyes for any reason, it's best to use ordinary cold water that has been boiled and then refrigerated. This simple treatment is the purest and the best eyewash you can use. However, if you prefer the refreshing feeling of an eyewash—which may disturb the natural film that covers, protects, and lubricates the eye—try one of my natural eyewash recipes (see pages 112–14) for a soothing change. Of course, if your eyes smart, burn, or feel gritty consistently, consult your eye doctor.

WHEN EYES ARE AFFECTED BY BRIGHT LIGHTS

I don't pretend to know all the medical explanations for certain remedies, but for centuries castor oil has been used both externally and internally for eye care. In reading Barbara Goldsmith's book *Little Gloria Happy at Last*, the life story of Gloria Vanderbilt, I was amused to see my trusty castor oil eye cure mentioned. Gloria's mother, also named Gloria, had a twin sister, Thelma (who, by the way, later became the mistress of the Prince of Wales). One day the girls had a small part in a film called *Northern Lights* starring Marion Davis. The lights on the set, called Klieg lights, affected Thelma's eyes badly and the doctor diagnosed it as a case of "Klieg eyes"—an irritation caused by exposure to excessively hot and bright lights. For days, the story continues, Gloria dripped castor oil into Thelma's eyes to make them feel better.

HOW TO HANDLE EYEBROW DANDRUFF

Can you actually get dandruff in your eyebrows and even your eyelashes? The answer is yes. Seborrhea, commonly known as dandruff, can affect both brows and lashes, making them appear dark and greasy. This condition can be treated with a medicated, antidandruff shampoo. However, as seborrhea is a medical problem and not a cosmetic one, it's best to consult your dermatologist or eye doctor.

How Safe Are Eye Drops?

Eye doctors will tell you that decongestant eye drops, used occasionally, are not harmful. However, overuse or frequent use of eye drops can cause redness to develop in the eyes. Unfortunately, it is impossible to determine in advance what the limit for each person will be, so the safest advice is to use eye drops very sparingly.

When Your Eyes and Head Are Aching

From time to time we all get headaches. If you are like me and dislike taking pain killers because they make you feel drowsy, try giving yourself a relaxing massage. It's a much healthier way of getting rid of pain and reducing tension. Here's how:

First, massage all pressure points above the eye. Use the ball of your thumb or middle finger to apply pressure to spots along the eyebrows and at each temple. Use light pressure above the eyesocket and below the eyes. Then work on top of the head, starting at the hair line and moving back to the crown. Use heavy pressure here with two or three fingers. Then work all the way back to the base of the skull, including the top of your shoulders. Keep this massage going until your eyes feel more relaxed and your headache starts to fade.

Exercising Your Eyes

How do you keep eyes bright and healthy? Most doctors insist the best way is by getting enough sleep, keeping your body healthy—both inside and out—having a healthy mind, and, of course, eating a balanced diet. If you do these things regularly, you certainly have a good jump on beautiful, shining eyes. However, there are a few exercises, or beauty "boosts," you can do to give you that extra muscle strength you need to keep a firm skin tone, especially around the eye areas.

Good muscle tone is the key to keeping eye skin taut, and good muscle tone relies on understanding how muscles work. Whether they are face muscles or foot muscles, all muscles work in the same way. Actually, they operate in teams. If one muscle has the job of opening the eye, another muscle is responsible for closing it. When one muscle contracts, its teammate expands. To keep muscle pairs operating in sync we have to use both muscles of the team or we run the risk of becoming "one-sided"—and one-sided in facial muscle tone can mean frown lines, sagging lids, and many other expressions that become cemented in place because their equal and opposite reaction never happens.

Since the condition of the muscles beneath the skin determines your outer skin tone, exercising those muscles will go a long way toward helping you restore and maintain a more youthful look to your face.

The following eye exercises will help you firm up the all-important facial muscles that keep your eyes looking great. Don't be lazy about doing these exercises and don't let your friends or family dissuade you with comments that you look silly doing them. If you think you look silly doing these facial gyrations, just remember that out-of-tone muscles create a saggy skin texture (just as exposure to the sun does) which, in turn, ultimately leads to lines and wrinkles. So I urge you to try these fast and easy exercises. After all, they cost nothing, require no equipment, and you can do them anywhere at anytime. I find that sitting in bed, either in the morning or evening, is a very relaxing time and perfect for doing facial exercises. If you devote a quick five minutes each day to these exercises, you should begin to notice results within a few weeks.

For Crow's-Feet

Consciously controlling the opening and closing motions of your eye will help tone the muscles surrounding the eye and help prevent crow's-feet. We open and close our eyes hundreds of times a day but that's reflex action rather than controlled action. In order to make this open-close eye movement pay off for you and result in better, firmer muscle tone, you need to perform the actions consciously and deliberately.

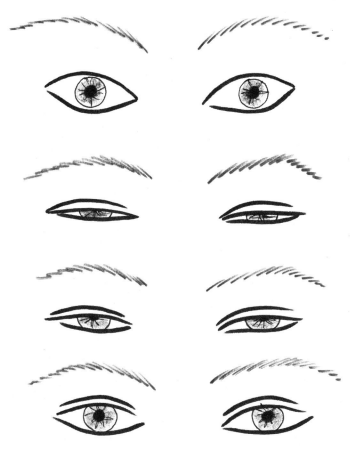

Technique: Open your eyes as wide as possible. Exaggerated motion is part of effective exercise. Hold your wide-eyed position for a few seconds and then slowly, very slowly, begin closing the eyes by bringing the upper and lower lids closer together. When your lids are almost touching, with just a sliver of space between them, start opening the eyes once again, but very slowly, almost as if you were pushing against weights on each lid. Repeat five times.

FOR DROOPY EYELIDS

Eye muscles work to keep your upper eyelids up, despite Newton's law of gravity. It's important to keep these muscles in good tone and this simple exercise will help to do just that.

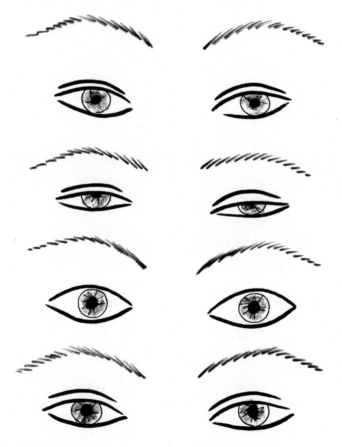

Technique: Raise your eyebrows very high in an exaggerated expression of surprise. Hold the brows in this position for a few seconds. Now, lower your upper eyelids to midpoint down the eye. Remember to keep your brows high while you do this. Slowly raise the eyelids back up until your eyes are wide open and you can see the whites of the eyes above the iris. Repeat three times.

FOR UNDEREYE PUFFINESS

We roll our legs and arms and torsos to keep them in shape, so why not our eyes as well? The rolling and blinking action of this easy exercise works the lazy, lower lid muscle of the eye to give it tone and strength. Here it goes!

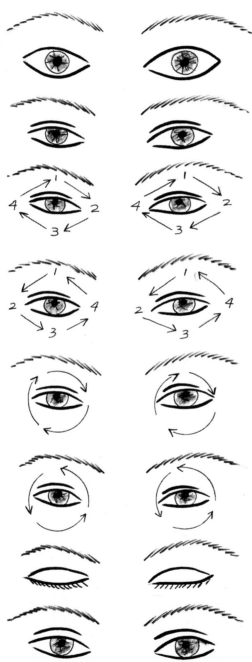

Technique: Open up your eyes as wide as possible. Really stretch them open and hold them that way for several seconds. Relax back to their normal position. Roll your eyes around as if you were checking out the four corners of your room or wall. Repeat three times. Now roll them around smoothly, in a circle; first, rolling them to the right and then to the left. When you have finished these rolling motions, start blinking the eyelids—hard. Keep them tightly shut for a few seconds. Open up and then repeat. Repeat entire exercise three times.

FOR FROWN LINES

Most faces are very expressive and that's what helps us communicate our feelings. However, we sometimes get stuck with permanent "expression lines" where we don't want them and frown lines fall under that heading. We probably never stop to think about the muscles responsible for making frowns, but they work by pulling the eyebrows together and then downward. This exercise concentrates on the opposite set of muscles—those that spread the brows apart to their natural position.

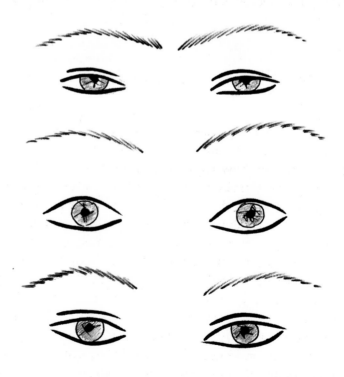

Technique: Start by frowning as hard as you can. Hold that intense frown expression for a few seconds; really force the eyebrows together. Next, lift the eyebrows up as high as you possibly can. This will relax the brows. If you prefer, you can do this exercise looking directly into a mirror. Repeat five times.

Maintaining Youthful Eyes

You're never too old to become younger —
MAE WEST

This quote says it all. Yes, there are ways to have perennially youthful-looking eyes at any age—if you're willing to work at it. Your eyes are one of the most sensitive areas anywhere on your body so they must be treated with the utmost care, especially as you get older and your body system begins to slow down. If you really want your eyes to look younger in years than they actually are, you need to pay particular attention to a few special aspects of your everyday living. The first such aspect is diet.

DIET FOR THE OVER-40 WOMAN

Nutritionists tell us "we are what we eat," and it's easy to spot bad eating habits as, sooner or later, they show up in poor skin tone and color, cloudy eyes, dull hair and other unattractive symptoms. Foods have a profound effect on how we look as well as on the health of our eyes. For example, visual problems associated with a mild lack of *vitamin A* include quick tiring of the eyes, sensitivity to bright lights and glare, dimness of vision at night, less acute day vision, and susceptibility to such infections as sties and conjunctivitis. When we don't get sufficient quantities of the *B-complex vitamins* in our daily diet, more eye problems including sensitivity to bright light, eyes that water readily, and eye strain accompanied by a bloodshot appearance, can occur. If the vitamin B deficiency becomes acute, the skin at the outer corners of the eyes may split and the eyes burn and become fiery red. *Vitamins C, D,* and *E* are also extremely important to eye health, especially vitamin E, which is an indispensable aid in helping prevent wrinkling of the delicate eye skin area. It has been shown that wrinkles can be prevented by giving large amounts of vitamin E—a statistic, whether true or not, which started me taking a vitamin E tablet every morning and night.

In addition to these internal vitamin nourishers, you also need to drink lots of fresh water every day—a minimum of eight glasses. I prefer bottled water, and drink several quarts throughout the day. I keep a carafe on my desk at work and on my night table at home. If you prefer to save money or simply want to make your own bottled water, boil tap water and refrigerate it. It's economical, pure, and doesn't contain any additives.

MOISTURIZERS FOR YOUTHFUL-LOOKING EYES

A woman is *never too young* to start moisturizing the skin areas around her eyes, since these areas contain only a tiny bit of oil and are one of the first places on your face to dry out and crease. Aging eyes, in particular, need an extremely good cream treatment—daily. Apply a rich moisturizer to the bone that surrounds the eye, on the lid, and under the eye. Pat on gently with your ring finger, as this finger exerts the least amount of pressure on your skin and keeps any harsh pulling and tugging to a minimum.

AGE-RETARDING MASSAGES   These gentle massage techniques, used in conjunction with eye creams, will help to beautify eyes that are beginning to show signs of age:

For laugh lines: Gently massage with moisturizer upward over the upper cheek toward the outer corner of the eye. Use more cream to delicately pat the undereye area from the nose bridge out to the temples.

For crow's-feet: Massage with cream upward from the temples and from the middle of the forehead toward the hairline. Stroke upward with both hands, each going in an up and out direction toward opposite temples.

EYE MAKEUP FOR THE OVER-40 WOMAN

One of the fastest and surest ways to make your eyes appear older is to use eye makeup improperly. I have seen women add as much as ten years to their faces simply by using the wrong type of eye shadow or applying liner poorly. Here are a few easy makeup tricks to help ensure that your eyes will look as young and beautiful as you feel.

• *Always apply eye shadow over a creamy eye base you have put on your lids.* This will help keep them lubricated and prevent the shadow from drying out and creasing.

• *Apply eye shadow with a soft brush only* to avoid any harsh stretching of the delicate skin area surrounding the eyes.

• If you like to use liner for extra emphasis, *apply liner with a fine-pointed brush only.* Place the brush on the base of the lashes starting at the inside corner of the eye and bring the line to the outer corner of the eye in short sweeping strokes. Avoid doing what so many women do—stretching out the lid before applying the liner. This leads to a hard, straight-line look that, in addition to being too rough on the delicate skin, also creates a "fake," unattractive line—just the kind an older woman should avoid.

• *Always line the inside rims of your eyes with kajal* as this will draw attention to the eye (and away from other distractions aging may cause), define the shape of the eye, and make the whites of your eyes appear whiter and more youthful.

• *Avoid mascaras with fibers or thickening agents,* as these formulas tend to dry out and flake. Even worse, they will eventually dry your lashes to the point where they become brittle and can break off.

• *Remove your eye makeup very, very gently.* Use a mild, not-too-oily eye makeup remover; otherwise you'll spend a lot of time removing the oil from the eye area—a must in order to apply eye makeup properly. Remove eye makeup only with a soft cotton ball. Never use a tissue for this purpose, as tissues contain harsh fibers that are damaging to sensitive older skin.

WHAT ABOUT COSMETIC SURGERY?

One can't talk about aging eyes without at least mentioning plastic surgery, commonly used to rejuvenate the face. If you are not the coward I am and insist on pursuing youth via surgery, I strongly suggest that you seek out a highly qualified surgeon to do the job. Check his or her credentials thoroughly before you decide. Don't be charmed by a personality; medical training, prior experience, and hospital and professional accreditations are the most important factors. And don't make your choice quickly. Talk with at least two or three specialists. The consultation fees are worth the end result.

Though a controversial procedure, cosmetic surgery has its positive points, the most obvious being the creation of "instant youth." However, there are risks involved with short-circuiting nature and women should be aware of these before they sign on the dotted line. Plastic surgery, whether for saggy eyelids, dipping jowls, or even an oversized nose, is still surgery—and no surgery is minor. Complications are always possible and the opposite of what you expected can result. In addition, the operation will cause temporary discomfort and bruising and commonly leaves scarring. Of course, a skilled surgeon will conceal the scar as much as possible by making the incision in a skin fold, for example, but certain procedures will scar heavily no matter how skilled the surgeon who performs them.

The most common surgical cosmetic procedure for eyes is called Blepharoplasty, or eyelid surgery, an operation which can be performed by itself or as part of a face lift. The incision is made in the fold of the lid and the excess fat and skin are removed. A procedure similar to this is used to eliminate bags under the eyes; the incision is made just below the lower lashes. At the same time, an eyebrow lift may be performed, with the incision just at the upper edge of the eyebrow. This helps reduce furrows around the eyes. A chemical peel, which is really a controlled "burn" of the outer skin layer, may be done to remove crow's-feet or expression lines.

I'm sure you know by now that I am a "beauty by natural means" woman. Rather than relying on corrective procedures like surgery, I prefer the artistic use of makeup accompanied by good diet. To me, this unbeatable twosome is far more effective in achieving a more youthful, attractive appearance than any artificial means could ever be. And, by using only your own good health and makeup ingenuity, you will retain that most special beauty element of all—your own unique you.

French fashion designer Yves Saint Laurent once said "The most beautiful makeup of a woman is passion, but cosmetics are easier to buy." I concur completely!

Eyescope

ARIES (March 21–April 19)
You will never know from the expression of the Aries eye what Arians are thinking. They are honest, very dependable, and good friends to have.

TAURUS (April 20–May 20)
Taurians like to surround themselves with beauty. Loyalty shines out from this eye. If you have a Taurian for a friend, you are very lucky.

GEMINI (May 21–June 21)
The Gemini eye portrays innocence while at the same time disguising a lust for life and very adventurous feelings. Geminis are provocative, sexy, and extremely alluring.

CANCER (June 22–July 22)
Cancers have very peaceful eyes. When you look into their clear eyes, a soothing and relaxing sensation will overcome you.

LEO (July 23–August 22)
The Leo lady likes a lot of color in her eye makeup because she likes to be the center of attraction, the star of every show. Loving warmth radiates from Leo eyes.

VIRGO (August 23–September 22)
Virgos project a neat, clean, and tidy appearance at all times. It's part of their lifestyle. Their quiet eyes often hide much deeper feelings.

LIBRA (September 23–October 22)
One look from a Libran eye and you are held captive, for this eye can charm the birds right out of the trees! Librans are notorious for talking with their eyes. Their innermost thoughts and expressions are revealed through their eyes.

SCORPIO (October 23–November 21)
You can never tell what thoughts lie behind the Scorpian eye despite the fact that it is one of the most passionate and affectionate signs in the zodiac. Very secretive, sometimes too blunt for their own good, Scorpians can make their dreams come true.

SAGITTARIUS (November 22–December 21)
Sagittarians like to surround themselves with vibrant colors, including on their eyes. They are gregarious, flamboyant, hospitable, and a comfort to have near you. The gentle warmth of their eyes puts others instantly at ease.

CAPRICORN (December 20–January 19)
This is a very determined, alive eye. Capricorns are ambitious go-getters who set high goals for themselves and are usually able to drink every drop from the cup of life. Behind their warm eyes twinkles a delightful sense of humor.

AQUARIUS (January 20–February 18)
Aquarians are sociable and generous. This eye can be extremely flirtatious, but watch out because it can be very fickle too. Aquarians have honorable intentions and will always look you straight in the eye.

PISCES (February 19–March 20)
The Pisces eye is one full of romantic promise. As the dreamers of the zodiac, Piscean women make sensuous, tender lovers.

Index

Aching eyes, 127
Aging eyes, 42–43, 134–36
  cosmetic surgery and, 135–36
  "crepy," 16, 50
  diet and, 133–34
  makeup tricks for, 16, 134–35
  massages for, 134
  See also Crow's-feet; Expression lines;
    Wrinkles
Air travel, eye beauty tips for, 122–23
Allergies to cosmetics, 125
Almond eyes, 33–34
Applying eye makeup, step-by-step proce-
  dure for, 45–46
Apricot Anti-Wrinkle Cream, 117
At-home eye makeup, 86

Beauty, eye makeup and, 3–5, 31
Beauty marks ("les mouches"), 83–85
Beauty recipes, 104–20
  for the body, 120
  for the eyes, 105–14
  for the face, 115–18
  for the hair, 119–20
  for the hands, 118–19
Beauty rest, 108, 123, 124
Bee Sting Icer (eye tonic), 110–11
B. H. Krueger, xiv
Black-brown eyes, 65
Black eye, yellow apple remedy for a, 110
Black women's complexion, 68
Black women's eyes, 41–42
Blemishes, beauty recipes for, 115, 118
Bloomingdale's, xiv
Blue eyes, 61
Bride, eye makeup for the, 87
Bright lights, 126, 133
Brown eyes, 60
Brushes
  cosmetic, 17–18

Brushes *(cont'd)*
  eyebrow, 10
  eye shadow, 18, 49
Butterfly eye, 76–77

Carrot Eye Oil, 107
Carrot Juice, 111–12
Castor oil
  as eye drops, 126
  Scented (eyelash lengthener), 114
Chamomile Compress, 108–9
Citrus Squirt Eyewash, 113
Cleansers, home-made facial, 115, 118
Close-set eyes, 38–39
Clothes, *see* Fashion colors
Color
  contouring with, 49–50
  experimenting with, 57–59
  eyeglass fashion and, 93–96
  highlighting with, 50
  importance of, 4, 56–57
  Pyramid Color Plan, 57–59
  See also Eye color; Fashion colors
Complexion
  "colorless," improving, 121–22
  eyeglass frames and, 93–94
  makeup color and, 58, 66–69
Concealing cream, 12
  applying, 47–48
Confidence, 3
Contact lenses, 98–99
  eye makeup and, 99
Contouring, 49–50
Corrective tricks
  for different eye types, 33–43
  tinted eyeglass lenses and, 96
  for tired or irritated eyes, 113–14
  See also specific eye types
Cosmetic allergies, 125
Cosmetics, *see* Equipment; *and specific items*

Cosmetics, home-made, *see* Beauty recipes
Cosmetic surgery, 135–36
Cotton balls, 9
Cotton-tip swabs, 9, 46
Creams
  massage, home-made, 120
  moisturizing, home-made, 117–18
  See also Eye cream; Moisturizers
Crepy eyes, 16, 50
Crow's-feet, 105
  exercise for, 129–30
  massage techniques for, 134
  temple pieces and, 93
Cucumber Cooler (eye tonic), 109
Curler, eyelash, 8

Dandruff, eyebrow, 126
Day-into-night switch, 74
Daylight, *see* Light conditions
Daytime eye makeup
  five-minute mistake-proof, 44–53
  light conditions and, 44
  touch-up for, 54
  for work, 85–86
Deep-set eyes, 38, 50
Diet, eye care and, 133–34
Different-sized eyes, 42
Drinks, healthy-eye, 111–12
Drooping eyes, 39
  exercise for, 130

Eastern eye, 78
Endive Juice, 112
Equipment
  eye cosmetic tools, 9–19
  eye maintenance tools, 7–9
  See also specific items
Evening eye makeup, 71–85
  basic, 72–73
  beauty marks ("les mouches") and, 83–85
  five beautiful looks for, 75–79
  gala eye, 86–87
  instant switch from daytime makeup to, 54
  light conditions and, 44
  special effect theatrics for, 81–85
Exercises
  for crow's-feet, 129
  for droopy eyelids, 130
  for undereye puffiness, 131
Expression lines
  exercise for, 132–33
  massages for, 134
  See also Crow's-feet; Wrinkles
Eyebrow brush, 10
Eyebrow dandruff, 126
Eyebrow pencil, 9
Eyebrows, 21–27
  applying color to, 9, 10, 46–47
  dye for, home-made, 113

Eyebrows *(cont'd)*
  electrolysis for, 26
  eyeglasses and, 100–1
  fullness of, 24
  grooming, 10, 46–47
  length (stop and start) of, 22–23
  shape (arch) of, 22
  tips for, 27
  tweezing, 25–26
  waxing, 26
Eyebrow scissors, 8
Eye care, 121–36
  for the aging eye, 133–36
  exercises for, 128–33
Eye color
  makeup color and, 58–59
  See also specific eye colors
Eye cream
  Madeleine's Own Home-Made, 107
  night, 54
  See also Moisturizers
Eye drops, 127
Eye exercises, *see* Exercises
Eyeglasses, 88–98, 100–3
  basic guidelines for, 101–3
  care of, 97
  eye makeup and, 100–1
  factors in selecting, 88–89
  as an investment, 97
  special-use, 98
  See also Contact lenses; Eyeglass frames; Eyeglass lenses
Eyeglass frames
  color and, 93–94
  face shapes and, 89–93
Eyeglass lenses
  color or tinted, 94–96
  types of, 96–97
Eye injuries, 125
Eyelash comb, 10
Eyelash curler, 8
Eyelashes, 28–30
  applying mascara to, 52–53
  conditioning for, 29
  curling your, 8, 52
  dyeing, 30
  false, 29
  lengthener, home-made, 114
  lengthening technique for, 28, 114
  separating, 10
Eyelid Lift (eye tonic), 111
Eyelids, exercise for droopy, 130
Eye liner, 51
  See also Kajal; Kohl
Eye makeup removers, 53
Eye pads, 108
Eye shadow, 12–13
  applying, 13
  color pencils, 16
  See also Color

Eye shadow brush, 18, 49
Eye shadow sponge applicator, 18
Eye tonic, 108–11
Eye type
    corrective tricks for, 33–43
    determining your, 32–33
    eyeglass frames and, 89
    See also specific eye types
Eyewashes, 112–13, 126
Eye-White Wonder, 113

Face, beauty recipes for the, 115–18
Face shapes, eyeglasses and, 89–93
Facial exercises, 128–33
Facial Mask, Honey 'n' Egg, 118
Facial scars, 123
Fair complexion, 66
False eyelashes, 29
Fashion colors
    eyeglasses and, 93–96
    makeup color and, 58–59, 69–70
Fontaine, Joan, 28
Foreign substance in the eye, 125
Foster, Aida, 3, 56
Freckled complexion, 66–67
Freckles, "Take-Away" Lotion for, 118
Frown lines, exercise for, 132–33

Gala eye, 86–87
Geranium Hair Rinse, 120
Gilded eye, 75–76
Girls, first eye makeup for, 87
Glasses, *see* Eyeglasses
Glitter, 81–83
Green eyes, 58–59, 64

Hair, beauty recipes for, 119–20
Hair color, eyeglass frames and, 93–94
Hand moisturizers, home-made, 118
Hats, eyeglasses and, 102
Hazel eyes, 62
Headaches, massage for, 127
Healthy-eye drinks, 111–12
Heart-shaped face, eyeglass frames and, 91
Henri Bendel, xiii, xiv
Hideaway (concealing cream), 12, 47–48
Highlighting pencil, 16
Highlighting the eyes, 50
Honey Hand Lotion, 118
Honey 'n' Egg Facial Mask, 118

"Idaho Rub," 115
"Indian Eyes," xv
    See also Kajal; Kohl
Indian Hair Conditioner, 119
Iridescent eye shadow, 12–13
Iridescent (highlighting) pencil, 16

Jacobsen, Robert, xiv

Kajal (inside eye liner), 14–16
    applying, 51–52
Kaufman, Dr. Ira, 125
Kempster, Karol, xiv
Klieg lights, 126
Kohl (outside eye liner), 15–16
    applying, 37

Laugh lines, massage technique for, 134
Levene, Arthur, xiv, xv
Light conditions
    daytime eye makeup and, 44
    evening eye makeup and, 44, 71
    magnifying mirror and, 9
    See also Bright lights
Lining the eyes, 51
Lorgnettes, 102–3
Lubricants
    for eyebrows, 27
    for eyelashes, 29, 114
    See also Moisturizers

Madeleine Mono Ltd., xiv
Magnifying mirror, 8–9
Makeup carry kit, 19–20
Makeup removers, 53
Marigold Lotion, 118
Mascara, 11–12
    applying, 52–53
Massage Cream, Exotic, 120
Massages
    age-retarding, 134
    for headaches, 127
Matte color pencils, 16
Matte eye shadow, 12–13
Mayo Magic (hand tonic), 119
Mint Tea Eyewash, 112
Moisturizers
    aging eyes and, 134
    eye, home-made, 105–7
    facial, home-made, 117–18
    hand, home-made, 118–19
    See also Creams; Lubricants
Mono, Lily, 3
Mono, Madeleine, xiii–xv
Muscle tone, exercises for facial, 128–33

Narrow eyes, 36–37
Neck cushions, Chinese, 123
Night eye cream, 54
Night eyes, *see* Evening eye makeup

Older eyes, *see* Aging eyes
Olive complexion, 67
Olive Oil Soak, 106
Olivier, Sir Laurence, 56

Oriental eyes, 40–41
Oval face, eyeglass frames and, 91

Parsley Perk-Up (eye tonic), 114
Pear-shaped face, eyeglass frames and, 91
Pencils
    cosmetic, 14–16
    eyebrow, 9
    highlighting, 16
    inside eye liner (kajal), 14–16
    matte color, 16
    outside eye liner (kohl), 15–16
    Web Hand Test for, 14
Pencil sharpener, 18
Pencil Test for eyebrows, 22–23
Personality, color and, 57
Photographs
    Eye-White Wonder for, 113
    makeup considerations for, 87
Plastic surgery, 135–36
Potato Pamper (hand tonic), 119
Potato Paste (eye tonic), 110
Powdering the eyes, 48
Protruding eyes, 40, 50
Puffy eyes, 123
    exercise for, 131–32
Pyramid Color Plan, 57–58

Radiant rainbow eye, 77
Recipes, *see* Beauty recipes
Red-Eye Remedy, 111
Red, teary eyes, cosmetic allergies and, 125
Removing eye makeup, 53
Rest, 108, 123, 124
Rimming the eyes, 51–52
Rose Tonic (face refresher), 116
Round eyes, 34–35
Round face, eyeglass frames and, 91
Ruddy complexion, 67

Sage Tea Eyebrow Dye, 113
Saint-Laurent, Yves, 136
Salt Eyewash, 113
Scars, facial, 123
Scented Castor Oil (eyelash lengthener),
    114
Scissors, eyebrow, 8
Sedative, home-made natural, 108
Selznick, David O., 28
Skin coloration, *see* Complexion
Slant board, 122
Sleep, *see* Beauty rest

Small eyes, 35–36
South Sea Island Cream, 117
Special effect theatrics, 81–85
Special occasion eyes, 85–87
Spinach Juice, 112
Sponge applicator for eye shadow, 18
Sports
    eyeglasses for, 98
    eye makeup and, 86
Square face, eyeglass frames and, 91
Sultry eye, 79
Summer complexion, 68–69
Sunbathing, 69
    eye care tips for, 123–24
    tonic for irritated eyes and, 114
Sunglasses, 95, 98
Swanson, Gloria, 106
"Sweet Dreams" Cider 'n' Honey, 108

"Take-Away" Lotion (hand tonic), 118
Tanned complexion, 68–69
Tawny complexion, 67
Taylor, Elizabeth, 83
Tea Bag Tonic, 109
Teen-age girls, first eye makeup for, 87
Temple pieces, 92–93
Tinted eyeglass lenses, 94–96
Touch-ups
    carry kit for, 19–20
    thirty-second, 54
Tweezers, 6, 7
Tweezing procedure for eyebrows, 25–26

Violet eyes, 63
Vitamin A, 112, 117, 133
Vitamin B, 133
Vitamin C, 112, 133
Vitamin D, 133
Vitamin E, 107, 133–34
Vitamin E oil, 54, 107
Vitamin G, 112
V shape, contouring and, 50

Waterproof cosmetics, 11, 86
Web Hand Test, 14
Westmore, Mont, 28
Wide-set eyes, 37
Witch Hazel Magic (eye tonic), 110
Work, daytime eye makeup for, 85–86
Wrinkle Eraser (face tonic), 117
Wrinkles, beauty recipes for, 117
    See also Crow's-feet; Expression lines

About the Author

MADELEINE MONO, a British citizen by birth who now makes her home in America, is the recognized innovator and leader in eye cosmetics throughout the world.

Eyes and eye makeup have been a lifelong fascination for Madeleine Mono. She began experimenting with eye makeup and creating the beautiful color techniques her millions of fans have come to associate with her name when she was a professional actress on the British stage. In 1974, with an initial investment of $7500, she introduced her first eye makeup product — "Indian Eyes," a kajal pencil used for lining the lids of the eyes. The phenomenal success of this single product launched her cosmetic line and provided the groundwork for what is now an international cosmetics empire and includes a complete selection of eye makeup products.

To the legions of American women who use her products, the name Madeleine Mono has become synonymous with color and style — beautiful and elegant colors: colors that bring out a woman's beauty; colors that any woman can use to accent her personality and give her face the unique look that is hers alone. And though Madeleine has been widely copied, her eye makeup techniques and products have never been duplicated. Her eye cosmetics are used by hundreds of top makeup artists and models as well as by Jacqueline Onassis, Nancy Kissinger, Beverly Sassoon, Cher, Suzanne Pleshette, Beverly Johnson, and other women internationally renowned for their beauty and fashion sense.

Madeleine Mono is the mother of four children and two stepchildren. She and her husband reside in New York.